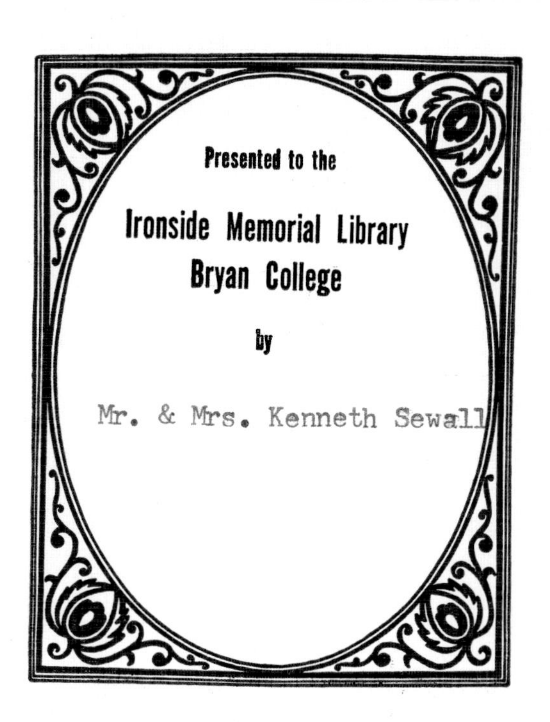
Presented to the
Ironside Memorial Library
Bryan College
by
Mr. & Mrs. Kenneth Sewall

WITHDRAWN

The twentieth century has seen biology come of age as a conceptual and quantitative science. Biochemistry, cytology, and genetics have been unified into a common framework at the molecular level. However, cellular activity and development are regulated not by the interplay of molecules alone, but by interactions of molecules organized in complex arrays, subunits, and organelles. Emphasis on organization is, therefore, of increasing importance.

So it is too, at the other end of the scale. Organismic and population biology are developing new rigor in such established and emerging disciplines as ecology, evolution, and ethology, but again the accent is on interactions between individuals, populations, and societies. Advances in comparative biochemistry and physiology have given new impetus to studies of animal and plant diversity. Microbiology has matured, with the world of viruses and procaryotes assuming a major position. New connections are being forged with other disciplines outside biology—chemistry, physics, mathematics, geology, anthropology, and psychology provide us with new theories and experimental tools while at the same time are themselves being enriched by the biologists' new insights into the world of life. The need to preserve a habitable environment for future generations should encourage increasing collaboration between diverse disciplines.

The purpose of the Modern Biology Series is to introduce the college biology student—as well as the gifted secondary student and all interested readers—both to the concepts unifying the fields within biology and to the diversity that makes each field unique.

Since the series is open-ended, it will provide a greater number and variety of topics than can be accommodated in many introductory courses. It remains the responsibility of the instructor to make his selection, to arrange it in a logical order, and to develop a framework into which the individual units can best be fitted.

New titles will be added to the present list as new fields emerge, existing fields advance, and new authors of ability and talent appear. Only thus, we feel, can we keep pace with the explosion of knowledge in Modern Biology.

James D. Ebert
Ariel G. Loewy
Howard A. Schneiderman

Modern Biology Series **Consulting Editors**

James D. Ebert
Carnegie Institution of Washington

Ariel G. Loewy
Haverford College

Howard A. Schneiderman
Case Western Reserve University

Published Titles

Burnett-Eisner	***Animal Adaptation***
Delevoryas	***Plant Diversification***
Ebert	***Interacting Systems in Development***
Griffin	***Animal Structure and Function***
Loewy-Siekevitz	***Cell Structure and Function***
Odum	***Ecology***
Ray	***The Living Plant***

Forthcoming Titles

Levine	***Genetics,*** *second edition*
Novikoff-Holzman	***The Cell and Its Organelles***
Savage	***Evolution,*** *second edition*
Sistrom	***Microbial Life,*** *second edition*

Behavior

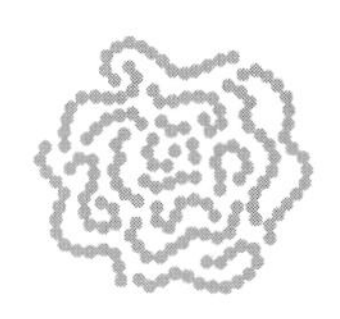

William G. Van der Kloot

New York University
School of Medicine

Holt, Rinehart and Winston, Inc.
New York Chicago San Francisco
Atlanta Dallas Montreal
Toronto London

Library of Congress Catalog Card Number: 68—13741
2677250
Printed in the United States of America
1 2 3 4 5 6 7 8 9

Text and cover design by Margaret O. Tsao
Illustrations by George V. Kelvin · Science Graphics

Preface

This book is an introduction to the most challenging problem in natural science, the analysis of the behavior of animals. The problem is difficult because behavior is the organized output of hundreds, thousands, millions, or billions of cells, interacting according to plans built into the cell array by the genetic heritage and by the past history of the animal. The problem is fascinating because the main lines of animal evolution are toward increasing behavioral complexity, so that now the animal kingdom even includes a species determined to understand its own behavior.

In spite of the interest and the challenge inherent in these problems, the study of behavior is just beginning to achieve the status given to other branches of biology.

Only the exceptional biology or zoology department offers a course in behavior. In biological journals, there are more papers dealing with the composition of the urine, with mitochondria, or with genes, than with behavior. It is worth taking a moment to discuss why behavior has developed so slowly as a branch of biology, since this is a good starting point for a survey of our present knowledge. The first reason is that many of the biologists in past generations believed that behavior was guided by forces which are beyond scientific analysis. Therefore, behavior could not be studied by the usual rules of science. These doubts have now been largely set to rest, partly because of the progress which has been made in studying some aspects of behavior and partly because of the great successes scored in other areas of biology which once seemed unlikely to yield readily to experimental analysis.

An historical anomaly which slowed the growth of behavior study as a part of the biological sciences was the setting up of psychology as an independent discipline. Traditional psychology is oriented toward the study of human behavior. Animals are used as models of men rather than for their own sakes. In spite of this special viewpoint, psychologists made many of the most important advances in the study of behavior; any biologist interested in behavior would make a serious mistake in ignoring the contributions of the experimental psychologists.

Nevertheless, the teaching and study of behavior cannot be left entirely to the psychologists. Biologists who are interested in ecology or in evolution must understand the principles of behavior in order to understand their field. Conversely, the student of behavior can benefit from the special viewpoint of the field biologists. Some of the most interesting problems awaiting geneticists, developmental biologists, biochemists, and neurophysiologists involve the analysis of behavior. There is an urgent need for more behavior study in biology departments; and experimental psychology should be integrated more closely with the rest of biology, since fundamental differences in aims or methods have mostly vanished. To this end, no distinction will be made in this book on the basis of the department to which an investigator is affiliated.

Scientific endeavor can be undertaken on two levels. On the first level, the investigator tries to establish consistent rules—or laws—that are obeyed by the system being studied. To choose a single example, Mendel showed that heredity could be approached by using a simple scheme. These basic laws are the foundation of the whole of classical genetics, with its proven methods for analyzing and predicting genetic events. On the second level, a problem is analyzed in terms of simpler or more elementary systems. For example, the understanding of the genetic apparatus in terms of the nucleotide sequence in the DNA molecule. It is worth noticing that both levels of analysis are useful and important, that one level never replaces the other, and that some understanding at the first level is a prerequisite for understanding the second.

Behavior can be treated in the same two ways. Some investigators are interested in discovering the laws that govern behavior. Others are interested in analyzing the genetics of behavior, the development of behavior, or the ways in which behavior is produced by the nervous system. Both levels of investigation are useful and fruitful; they will be intermingled in the pages of this book.

Advanced students of a science should know something about its history. The history of the behavioral sciences is filled with arguments over the difficult problems of finding an effective and balanced approach to the subject. There were many schools, debates, and divisions. My opinion is that a recital of these schisms is unnecessary in an introductory book. I have tried to approach the subject with a broad viewpoint, while avoiding replays of the debates of yesterday. The disadvantage in this method is that there is no place for giving credit to the many investigators who were responsible for developing the frame of reference which is the starting point for contemporary investigations.

W. G. V.
New York
January 1968

The motor individual is driven from two sources. The world around it and its own lesser world within. It can be regarded as a system which in virtue of its arrangement does a number of things and is so constructed that the world outside touches triggers for their doing. But its own internal condition has a say as to which of the things within limits it will do, and how it will do them. Its own internal condition is also initiator of some of its acts.

C. S. Sherrington,
Man on His Nature, 1940

Contents

Preface *v*

1 *Cocoon Construction* *1*

2 *Reflexes* *16*

3 *Reflexes and the Behavior of Coelenterates* *43*

4 *Three Sense Organs* *52*

5 *Sensory Abilities and Behavior* *64*

6 *Learning* *87*

7 *Motivation* *109*

8 *The Development and Genetics of Behavior* *121*

9 *Social Behavior* *135*

10 *Evolution and Behavior* *151*

Index *163*

chapter 1

Cocoon Construction

The scientist first questions, then seeks answers by observation and experimentation. The essential first step is asking the appropriate question, but this is especially difficult in the study of behavior. The subject matter is vast, yet at the same time almost too familiar. Everyone observes the behavior of fellow man and animals; behavior is a routine part of life. Too often, however, we analyze our observations in terms of preconceived ideas, which may be as valid to the understanding of behavior as the speculations of a savage about the movements of the stars would be to the understanding of astrophysics. Unfortunately, it is easier to dispel erroneous ideas about the motions of the planets than about the activities of animals: the one is remote, the other close at hand.

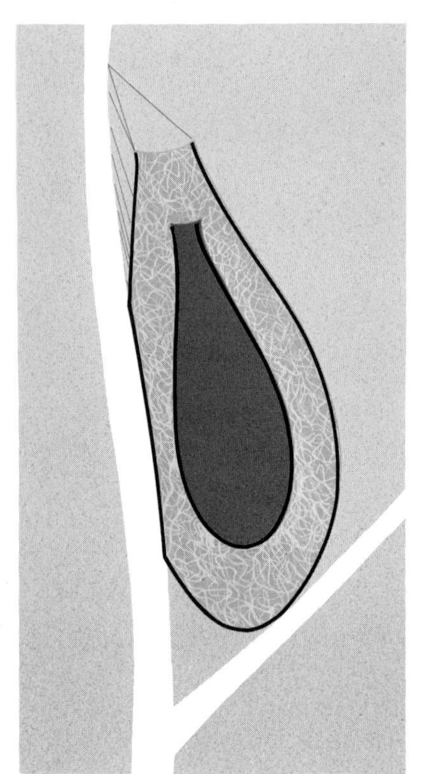

Fig. 1-1 *The structure of the cocoon spun by the giant American silkworm. There are three layers. A dense outer envelope, a loose spongy middle layer, and a dense inner envelope. The animal is enclosed within the inner envelope. Notice that the silk at the upper end of the outer and inner envelopes is loosely spun; the moth eventually pushes through these weak points to escape from the cocoon. (Adapted from E. J. Brill, Leiden,* Behaviour, *vol. V, 1953.)*

Therefore, it seems best to introduce the subject by choosing an example of behavior and using this example to point out the variety of experimental questions that may be profitably asked. Consider the example of a caterpillar spinning its cocoon. The caterpillar is the larva of the Giant American Silkmoth, a distant relative of the commercial silkworm. The caterpillar devotes much of its life to eating leaves and growing. Typical of animals with an exoskeleton, in order to grow, the caterpillar must periodically shed its old skin. At the time of each molt, the caterpillar stops feeding, wanders about until it finds a proper twig, and on this twig it spins a thin sheet of silk. The silk pad serves as an anchor for the old skin as it is pulled away. The caterpillar's life is interrupted four times by a larval molt; each time the animal which emerges from the shed skin is a caterpillar much like the one before.

At the end of the fifth and final stage in larval life, the caterpillar once again stops feeding, empties its guts, and begins to crawl about over the tree or shrub on which it has been living. Then it begins once again to spin out silk. But this time, instead of spinning a pad, the caterpillar weaves a single thread of silk, nearly a mile long, into a complicated cocoon. It is extraordinary that an animal can synthesize so long a thread of protein with the strength and durability that makes silk such excellent material for a tent. It is even more extraordinary

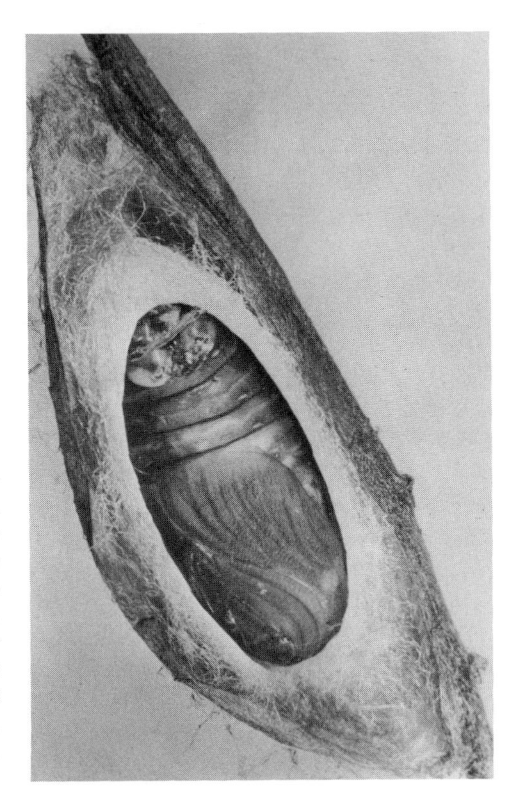

Fig. 1-2 *A cocoon that has been cut away to show the pupa within the inner envelope. This animal was allowed to spin the outer envelope and then the cocoon was turned upside down. The escape valve of the outer envelope points downward; the valve on the inner envelope points upward. (From E. J. Brill, Leiden,* Behaviour, *vol. V, 1953).*

that the caterpillar has the behavior to weave the thread into a complex cocoon, consisting of three distinct layers (Figure 1-1). The outer layer is a dense silken envelope, blunt at one end and pointed at the other. The middle layer is a spongy meshwork of silk. The dense inner envelope is a smaller version of the outer, blunt at one end and pointed at the other. Of thousands of cocoons collected from nature, it is rare to find one which deviates from this plan. Indeed, the structure of the cocoon is so characteristic of the species that it is an excellent taxonomic character. By simply looking at a cocoon, a competent naturalist can identify the genus and the species of the spinner. Cocoon spinning, therefore, is an example of species-specific behavior.

The cocoon is constructed from the outside in; and when it is finished, the caterpillar is snugly encased inside the inner envelope. A few days after the end of spinning the caterpillar molts once again, this time to the pupal stage, a form intermediate between the caterpillar and the moth (Figure 1-2). The pupa spends the winter inside of the cocoon in a state of developmental arrest. In the spring, development begins once again and three weeks later the pupal skin is shed, revealing the adult moth. The moth forces its way out of the cocoon by pushing through the pointed ends of the inner and the outer envelopes. At the pointed ends the silk is spun loosely and is readily pushed aside;

the pointed ends are valves which enable the animal to leave the cocoon. If someone ties the valves shut, the moth is imprisoned within the cocoon, unable to escape.

The moths normally live for only ten to fourteen days. They never feed; in fact, they have no digestive enzymes. The males fly about, while the females usually remain close to their cocoons, steadily releasing a powerful perfume. The male moth is astonishingly sensitive to this odor. Males are attracted from points down-wind more than a mile away. After mating, the fertilized eggs are laid on trees and shrubs around the place where the female emerged from her cocoon. The adults die, the tiny caterpillars hatch from the eggs, and the cycle begins once again.

THE TIMING OF SPINNING BEHAVIOR

Why is the cocoon spun at the end of the fifth stage of larval life and not at the time of any of the earlier larval molts? The answer to this question was discovered by an insect endocrinologist. Each of the molts, whether from larva to larva, from larva to pupa, or from pupa to adult, is triggered by the release of a hormone from a pair of glands in the thorax of the insect. The hormone from the thoracic glands, ecdysone, acts on the insect's tissues to bring about the changes associated with the molt. The release of ecdysone is, in turn, stimulated by a hormone secreted by a group of modified neurons in the insect's brain.

At the time of each of the larval molts, a second hormone is also circulating in the insect's blood. This hormone comes from a pair of tiny glands in the head, just behind the brain. It is called the juvenile hormone. The juvenile hormone has the remarkable property of braking progress in differentiation. If the juvenile hormone is present, the animal may molt, but it will make no progress in the life cycle. A caterpillar molts to the next larval stage. If a pupa is injected with a few micrograms of the hormone, it will molt to another pupa and not to a moth. The reciprocal experiment also works. If a small caterpillar is deprived of the juvenile hormone by the surgical removal of the glands, then at the next molt it will become a tiny pupa which continues to develop into a midget moth. The operated caterpillars also spin a tiny cocoon, identical except for size with the normal cocoon. The hormones control the morphogenetic progress of the animal and its behavior as well.

We do not know how the hormones act to control the caterpillar's behavior. They might act directly on the central nervous system. Or they might act on some peripheral tissue, such as the silk glands. The change in the silk glands could be reported to the central nervous system by a sense organ and thereby influence behavior. Hormones are known to affect behavior either by direct or by peripheral actions, which will be discussed in Chapter 7.

WHY BOTH VALVES ARE AT THE SAME END

There is a valve at the pointed end of the outer and of the inner envelope. If the cocoon should be constructed so that the valve of the inner envelope faces toward the blunt end of the outer envelope, then the moth will be trapped. I have never seen a cocoon spun in the wild in which the two valves were at opposite ends.

In the laboratory, it soon becomes clear that the valves of the outer and inner envelopes are spun facing upward. The observation suggests a simple experiment. A caterpillar is allowed to spin a normal outer envelope. Then the outer envelope is turned upside down. The valve of the inner envelope is then spun facing upward as usual; but this time the valves are at opposite ends of the cocoon and the moth is trapped. Gravity plays an important role in orienting the behavior of a spinning caterpillar.

Suppose that a caterpillar spins an outer envelope and then the cocoon is tilted so that it is oriented horizontally rather than vertically. The animal still spins the valve of the inner envelope at the same end as the valve in the outer envelope. Possibly the tapered shape of the outer envelope provides the cue for the proper orientation of the valve in the inner envelope. To test this idea, caterpillars were allowed to spin an outer envelope and were then removed and sewed in a small cloth bag, tapered at one end and blunt at the other. The cloth bags were laid on a horizontal surface. The valve of the inner envelope was always spun facing the tapered end of the bag.

When outer envelopes are tilted 135 degrees from the vertical, then sometimes the valve of the inner envelope is spun facing downward (the shape cue has determined the behavior) and sometimes the valve is spun facing upward (the gravitational cue has determined the behavior). In nature, where the outer envelope is spun facing upward, the shape and the gravitational cues work together to insure the proper location of the inner valve.

THE SEQUENCE OF SPINNING MOVEMENTS

The design of the cocoon is rigidly stereotyped. It is a map of the animal's behavior; it must be woven by a pattern of movements. Nevertheless, if you watch a caterpillar beginning to spin a cocoon, there seems to be little sense in the movements. The insect stretches, bends, and sways; the forepart of the body moves through sweeping arcs as the thread of silk is pulled from the spinneret. The movements at first seem to be without a pattern. It is surprising when an ordered structure begins to emerge from this seeming chaos.

The basic movements used to shape the cocoon can be deciphered by watching animal after animal spin in a simple setting. Perhaps the simplest possible environment is a rod fixed vertically in a small board. Caterpillars are persuaded to spin on this spinning platform by replacing them every time they wander off. After one to eight hours, the animals begin to spin.

Cocoon construction begins with the animal clinging to the rod, facing upward, with the tip of the abdomen just above the board. The caterpillar holds firmly to the rod with its five pairs of abdominal legs. The anterior part of the body is stretched upward and the silk thread is fastened to the rod. The forepart of the body is then bent downward and to the side; the silk thread is pulled out as the animal moves. The body continues to move in this arc until the head stretches to the furthest point of the baseboard which the animal can reach without moving its abdominal legs. At this point the silk is fastened to the baseboard. Repeating this pattern, an upward stretch followed by a downward bend produces a cone-shaped network of silken strands (Figure 1-3).

The downward bending is a vital part of the movement pattern. If a wooden block is placed on the spinning platform in such a way

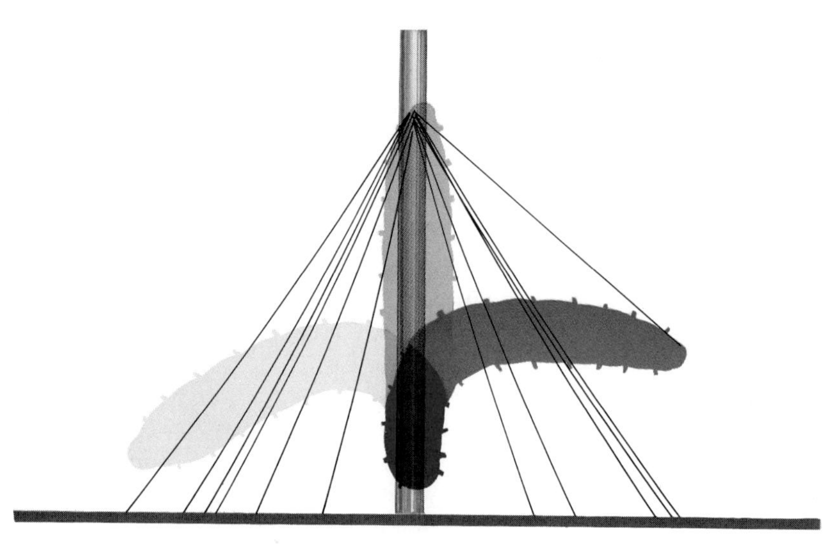

Fig. 1-3 *The movements of a spinning caterpillar when facing upward.*

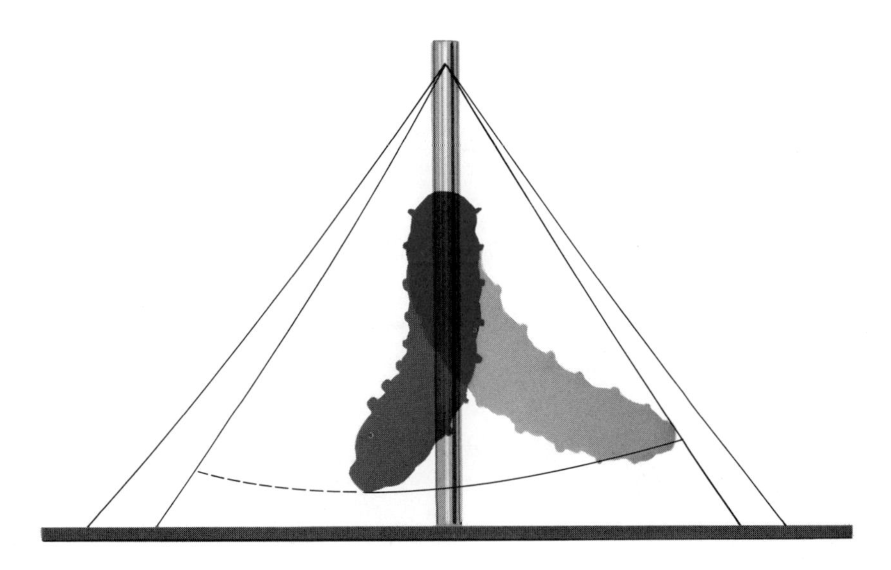

Fig. 1-4 The movements of a spinning caterpillar when it is facing downward.

that the silkworm encounters the block during a bend, the silk thread will be fastened to the face of the block. But the animal continues to bend until its body is maximally flexed; the movement is not ended with contact alone. This sequence of actions is called the stretch-bend movement pattern.

If the silkworm has bent its body until it is maximally flexed and has not encountered a surface to which the thread can be fastened, the animal remains flexed and sways about the anterior part of the body until it bumps into a surface. It is this swaying about that makes it so difficult to see order in the behavior of a silkworm in a natural environment, on the twigs of a tree, where the points for the attachment of silk are limited.

Periodically the silkworm turns its entire body around on the rod, so that it is facing toward the board. While facing downward, the caterpillar spins a relatively flat sheet of silk on the board, within the area bounded by the fibers of the cone of silk laid out previously. The second movement sequence is called the swing-swing pattern (Figure 1-4).

The animal alternates between the stretch-bend and the swing-swing patterns, which soon begin to produce the characteristic shape of the cocoon: tapered at the upper end and blunt at the lower end.

When the silkworm encounters a network of the silk already laid down, or a solid surface, it continues the basic movement pattern while also adding figure-eight movements of the head. These movements lay the silk as a meshwork, instead of a straight thread. This gives the envelopes of the cocoon their solid weave. At the apex of the cone of silk, there is not enough room for the silkworm to make the figure-eight movements. Consequently, at the apex of the envelope there are only

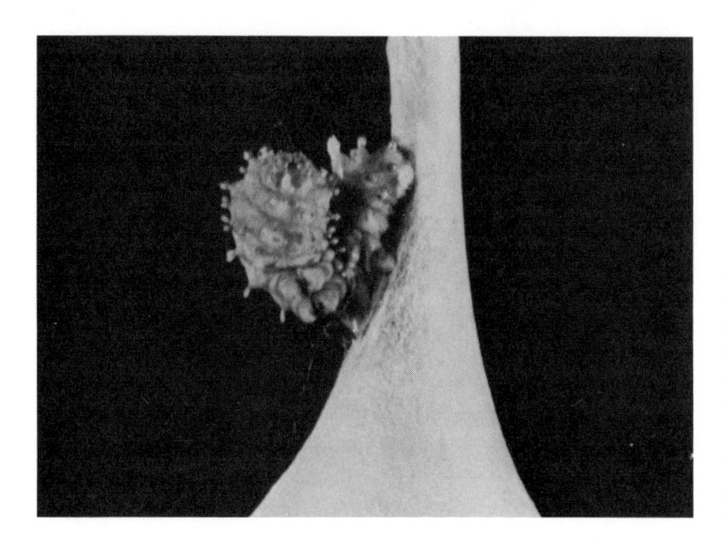

Fig. 1-5 *A caterpillar tied to the rod of a spinning platform so that it faces downward. The caterpillar uses the usual movements to spin a structure which looks something like a cocoon, but it is left outside. (From E. J. Brill, Leiden,* Behaviour, *vol. V, 1953.)*

vertical strands of silk, which can be pushed aside easily with the eraser end of a pencil. This localized weakness is the valve which serves, many months later, as the escape hatch for the moth.

The identification of the movement patterns advances our understanding of the way the cocoon is made and also suggests some further experiments. The silkworm can be tied to the rod, so that it always faces upward. These animals simply go ahead, perform the stretch-bend movement pattern as usual, and thereby produce a respectable-appearing cocoon.

When caterpillars are tied to the rod facing toward the board, they still periodically do the stretch-bend movements: stretching out to the furthest point on the baseboard which can be reached, fastening the silk thread, and then bending backward and fastening the thread to the rod alongside the abdomen (Figure 1-5). Once again, the caterpillar constructs a cone of silk, but this time, at the finish, the animal is still outside. The cone of silk spun by these animals is separated readily into two dense layers, enclosing a meshwork of silk. The two layers presumably correspond to the outer and inner envelopes—in this case, with the outside inside.

Silkworms can be sewn into a container of fine copper mesh, about the same size as a normal outer envelope but shaped like a cylinder, blunt at both ends. The animals spin an outer envelope directly on the copper gauze, with no hint of a tapered end. In this situation the behavior of spinning along a surface dominates over the stretch-bend movement pattern.

THE OUTER AND INNER ENVELOPES The next experiments were undertaken to see whether the external situation is important in changing the behavior so that the cocoon is divided into outer and inner envelopes. Silkworms taken from completed outer envelopes and allowed to begin again spin only an inner envelope. Caterpillars taken at the onset of spinning and sewed in the outer envelope stolen from another animal, spin a complete cocoon of their own. The external environment has little effect on when the silkworm spins an outer envelope and when an inner.

If a caterpillar is removed from a half-finished outer envelope and then made to begin again, it spins an outer envelope of half-normal thickness and then a normal inner envelope. The animal is going through an irreversible sequence of activities, which normally leads to the investment of about two thirds of the total silk in an outer envelope, and the remainder in an inner. This suggests that the silkworm begins the inner envelope when it has spun out a certain fraction of the silk. To check this idea, we tried to pull the first two thirds of the silk directly out of the spinneret. This experiment was doomed from the start, since the silk thread in the outer envelope is more than half a mile long. We were never able to pull out more than a few hundred feet before the thread broke.

Another way to approach the problem is to place the silkworm in an environment where it cannot construct a cocoon but will spin out its silk. For cocoon construction, the caterpillar must have points for attaching silk in all three dimensions. On a flat surface the silkworm can spin only a flat sheet. The easiest way to keep the caterpillar in a two-dimensional world is to put it inside a large inflated balloon. The silkworm spins a thin sheet of silk over most of the inside of the balloon. At any stage in spinning, the caterpillar can be taken from the balloon and placed in an environment where construction is possible. If about 60 percent of the silk has been spun as a flat sheet, then only an inner envelope will be spun. Silk spun as a flat sheet is equivalent, at all stages of the behavior pattern, to silk actually woven into a cocoon.

How does the animal measure the silk that has been spun? There are two possibilities: the caterpillar might measure either the amount of thread that has passed out or the amount of silk remaining in the glands. To determine the method used, we cut out part of the silk glands before spinning began. The silk glands are long convoluted tubes running down either side of the silkworm's body. If one of the silk glands is entirely removed, the operated silkworm spins a cocoon of normal architecture but of approximately half-normal weight. This is easy to understand since the thread is normally a fused double filament, one filament coming from each silk gland.

In another experiment, one silk gland was completely removed and the posterior part of the second gland was also cut out. The animals invariably began by spinning an outer envelope: if silk remained when the outer envelope was complete, construction of the inner envelope was begun. The animals never spun less than the usual amount of silk in the outer envelope, indicating that silkworms are able to measure the amount of silk thread which has been spun out. When a set amount has left the animal, construction of the outer envelope is stopped and construction of the inner envelope begins.

We were curious to know whether silkworms worked steadily while building their cocoon or paused occasionally to rest. Therefore, caterpillars were placed in a small cage of wire gauze, which was suspended on a thin wire stretching between two ring stands (Figure 1-6). A thin lever was fastened across the top of the cage; the lever traced on a smoked drum. We discovered that as the silkworm moves back and forth during the spinning, it shifts the center of gravity of the cage and the lever moves up and down on the smoked drum. The pattern traced on the slowly moving drum is surprisingly regular (Figure 1-7). The most significant feature of the record is the periodic major reversals. The reversals occur when the silkworm turns completely around in the cage, as it moves from the stretch-bend movement pattern to the swing-swing pattern. The smaller oscillations on the record represent the movements of the anterior part of the body during spinning. At the outset the silkworm turns around on the average of once every 40 minutes. After about twenty-five turnabouts, the cycle abruptly lengthens to around 170 minutes. The cycle probably lengthens when the animal begins work on the inner envelope.

Fig. 1-6 *The apparatus used for recording the movements of a silkworm placed within the small cylindrical chamber. When the animal moves the lever traces on the smoked drum. (Adapted from E. J. Brill, Leiden,* Behaviour, *vol. V, 1953.)*

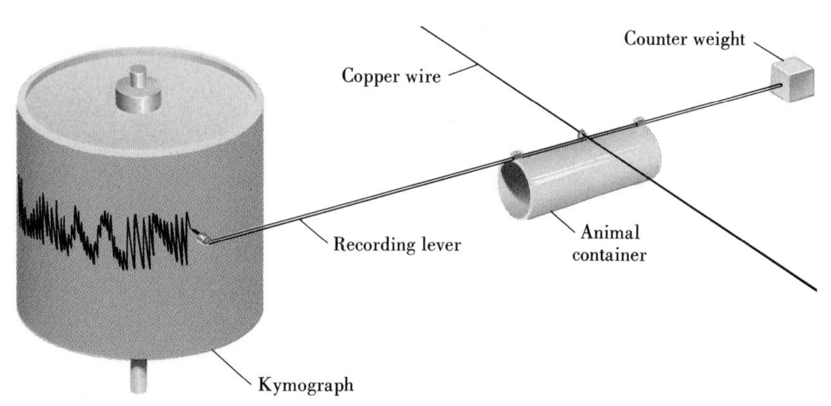

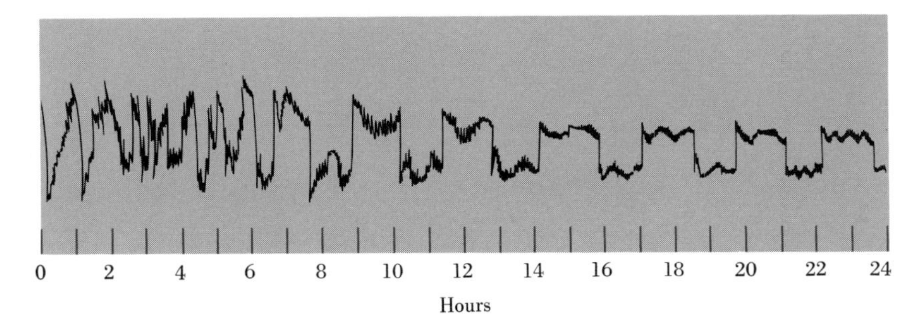

Fig. 1-7 Part of the record traced by a normal silkworm in the movement recorder. The periodic large shifts or reversals in the tracing are produced when the animal turns around its entire body. (Adapted from E. J. Brill, Behaviour, *vol. V, 1953.)*

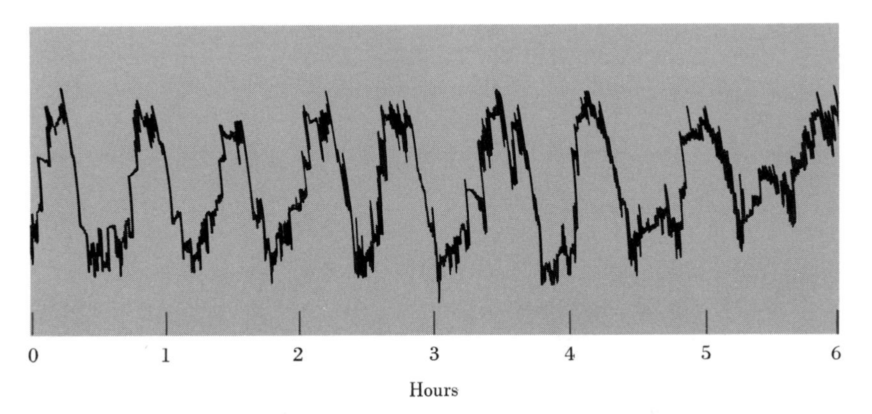

Fig. 1-8 A portion of the record traced by a silkworm whose spinneret was blocked with a dab of paraffin. Notice that the animal still turns around at regular intervals, just as though it were actually spinning. (Adapted from E. J. Brill, Leiden, Behaviour, *vol. V, 1953.)*

Silkworms whose spinnerets had been blocked with a dab of wax were placed in the movement recorder. During the next two days, these animals periodically turned around in the recorder, just as if they were spinning a cocoon (Figure 1-8). But the cycle duration in these animals was invariably 40 minutes; it never lengthened to the 170 minutes used during the spinning of the inner envelope. This result agrees with the theory that the shift to the spinning of the inner envelope takes place when a set amount of silk has been spun out.

But even when the animal is unable to spin out silk, there are periodic turnabouts. These animals cannot be turning whenever a set amount of silk is spun. We do not know how the timing of the turns is regulated. Perhaps the animal has a way of measuring time and turns around on the basis of this internal clock system (see Chapter 7).

Animals whose silk glands were removed surgically were also placed in the movement recorder. These silkworms move, crawl, and

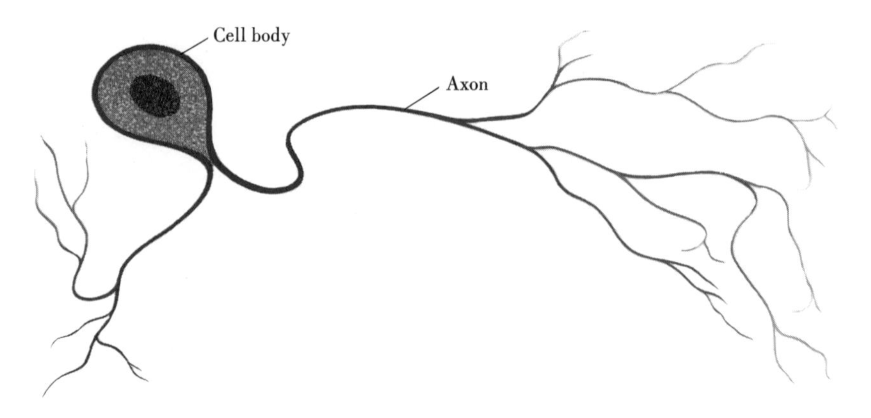

Fig. 1-9 *One type of nerve cell found in the insect nervous system.*

bend with considerable facility; they finish their life cycle without difficulty. However, their movements in the recorder are quite random; there is no sign of the rhythmic turnabout. Probably some sensory signal from the filled silk glands is an important stimulus for spinning behavior.

THE CENTRAL NERVOUS SYSTEM AND SPINNING

The parts of the central nervous system involved in the control of spinning behavior can be located by performing surgery on the central nervous system. The caterpillar's nervous system consists of a chain of ganglia, one in each segment of the animal's body. The ganglia contain the cell bodies of the nerve cells or neurons which make up the central nervous system (Figure 1-9). Each ganglion contains about 600 neurons. The ganglia are connected by the ventral nerve cord; the axons of the neurons run from ganglion to ganglion in the nerve cord (Figure 1-10). The largest ganglion is in the animal's head. It is formed by the fusion in embryonic life of three segmental ganglia. This is the silkworm's brain, or supraesophageal ganglion. It would be the same size as the heads of two pins placed side by side.

The brain is joined to the rest of the nervous system by two connectives. If these connectives are cut, all spinning is eliminated. When the nerve cord is transected between the abdomen and the thorax, the movements of the abdomen are no longer coordinated with the anterior part of the body. Nonetheless, these animals spin normal cocoons. As expected, the brain seems to play a special role in spinning behavior.

When only one of the two connectives between the brain and the rest of the nervous system is cut, the silkworms do spin; however, all of the silk is spun out as a flat sheet spread over every surface the caterpillar encounters.

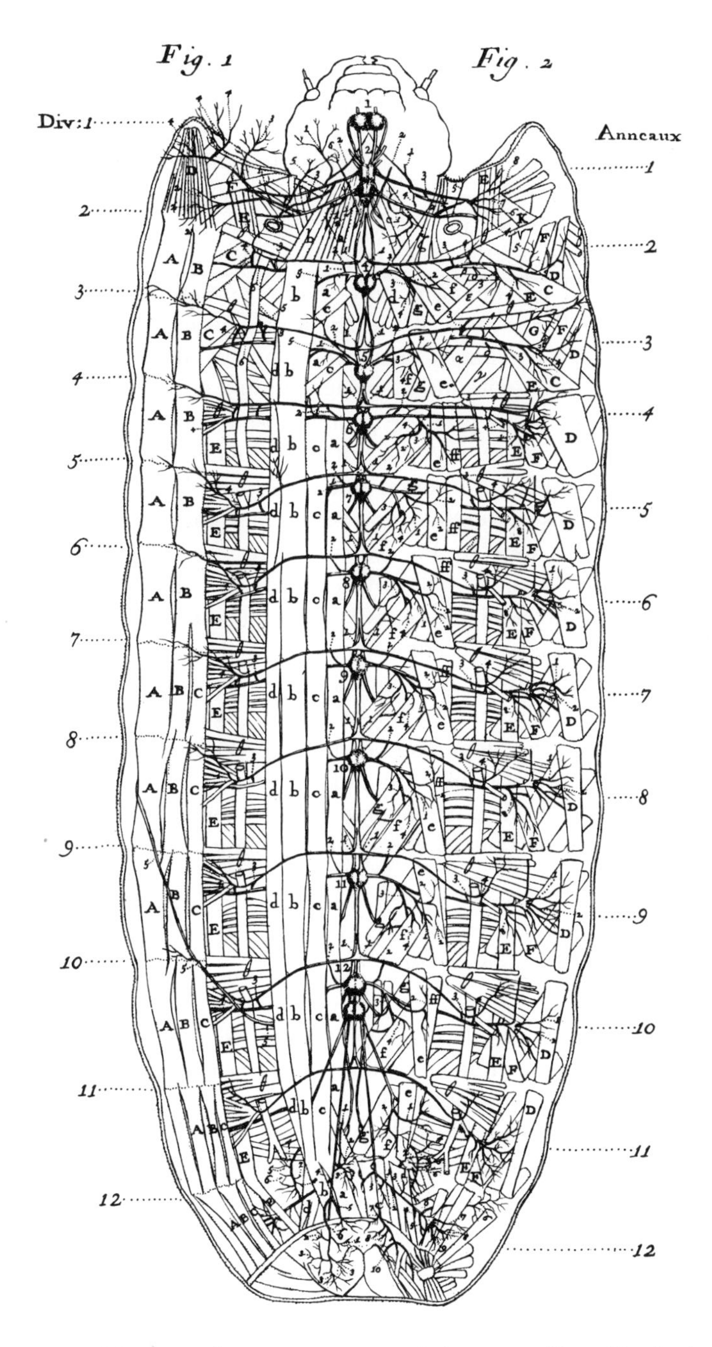

Fig. 1-10 *The central nervous system of the caterpillar. The brain is at the anterior end of the chain of ganglia. This figure is from a book on the anatomy of the goat-moth caterpillar which was published in The Hague in 1762. All of the dissections and illustrations are the work of P. Lyonet, a lawyer and amateur biologist (Photograph courtesy of Dr. Howard A. Schneiderman.)*

The brain can be divided into halves by a cut through the midline, which separates it into two hemispheres. Scores of nerve fibers cross from one side to the other across the midline. When these fibers are cut, the operated silkworms spin perfectly normal cocoons. Normal behavior from an animal whose brain is cut in half seems astonishing at first glance. Even in man the effects of a similar operation are subtle and not apparent to casual observation (see Chapter 5).

Smaller lesions of the brain can be made by burning local areas with a high frequency electrical cautery. Almost half of the brain can be burnt away without effecting spinning behavior. Lesions in the other half of the brain produce animals who spin their silk as a flat sheet; with some operations, the sheet is divided into two layers seemingly corresponding to the outer and inner envelopes of the normal cocoon. The regions essential for normal cocoon spinning seem to center around the part of the brain called the "mushroom bodies." The mushroom bodies of the insect brain are large groups of nerve cells, one in each hemisphere, whose cell bodies are on the posterior face of the brain. In the silkworm, the mushroom bodies comprise a relatively small part of each brain hemisphere. But in insects with highly developed behavior, such as the bees, wasps, and ants, the mushroom bodies are the dominant anatomical features of the brain. The fact that lesions of the mushroom bodies cause aberrant spinning behavior fits with the idea, from comparative anatomy, that this part of the brain is important in the coordination of complex behavior patterns of insects.

UNANSWERED QUESTIONS The experiments on spinning behavior have shown that the cocoon is woven by the use of two rather simple movement patterns. In a normal environment, the movements inevitably produce the characteristic cocoon; in abnormal environments the same movements produce distorted variants. There is no suggestion in the silkworm's behavior that the animal has any sort of built-in "picture" of the desired outcome of its actions. The animal does have a program of reactions to stimuli arising in its external and internal worlds; in a normal environment, the output is the cocoon.

Many of the most important questions about cocoon spinning remain unanswered. The cocoon is characteristic of the species of the spinner. Cocoon-spinning behavior must be passed from generation to generation as a genetic trait. The genetics of cocoon construction deserve an extensive investigation.

The development of spinning behavior also remains a total mystery. The silkworm spins only one cocoon during its life, so that at first glance there seems little reason to believe that any particular kind of experience is prerequisite for spinning behavior. In Chapter 6, examples are given of some of the subtle effects of everyday experiences on the development of some types of behavior. Every member of the species normally has experiences of the kind described. Reactions to these experiences lead to certain behavior patterns. A detailed developmental analysis is needed for a proper understanding of the animal's activities.

The study of the behavior of silkworms suggested that they detect the pull of gravity, and this stimulus helps in the orientation of the stretch-bend movement pattern and thereby of the valves. Sense organs must report the extent of stretching or bending of the body. The animal must also have a sensory system for measuring the amount of silk which passes out of the spinneret. The sense organs involved in these aspects of spinning behavior are not known and deserve investigation.

Throughout the period of spinning, the entire body is periodically turned around. Turning continues even when the spinneret is blocked and silk is not spun out. The silkworm must have at least a crude form of clock: some mechanism for estimating the passage of time, the nature of which is not known at present.

The brain is vitally important for spinning behavior, and we have a rudimentary idea of the regions of the brain involved. The central nervous mechanism for spinning behavior probably involves only a few thousand nerve cells; however, we do not know precisely how the individual cells interact to produce and regulate the movements of spinning behavior.

The point is this: for even a simple piece of behavior, there are more questions unanswered than answered. It is true that the problems of behavior are difficult. Any piece of behavior involves most of an animal, and any animal is a complicated thing. The challenges and difficulties in the analysis of behavior are obvious enough. But the amount of serious experimental effort so far devoted to the study of behavior is very small. There are many straightforward and interesting questions which have yet to be studied. Only an introduction to the study of behavior can be written, because the major part of the job remains to be done. The questions heavily outnumber the answers.

FURTHER READING

Van der Kloot, "Brains and Cocoons," *Scientific American* (April 1956), p. 131.

——, and C. M. Williams, "Cocoon Construction by the Cecropia Silkworm," Parts I and II, *Behaviour*, vol. 5 (1953), pp. 141, 157.

——, and ——, "Cocoon Construction by the Cecropia Silkworm, Part III, *Behaviour*, vol. 6 (1954), p. 233.

chapter 2

Reflexes

Some behavior is obviously triggered by events in the external world. A sharp rap on the tendon just below the knee cap almost invariably causes an extension of the lower leg. There is no difficulty in anticipating the behavior of a man who touches a hot stove. The event which initiates the behavior is called the stimulus, the action of the animal is the response, and the whole sequence of events from stimulus to response is a reflex.

The concept of the reflex has been a cornerstone in the description and analysis of behavior. Some investigators believed that all behavior might eventually be understood as a series of reflexes. This is too great a simplification: animals do more than simply respond moment by moment to changes in the external world. But the study of reflexes has led to important generalizations about behavior, and opened the way to revealing studies on the relation between behavior and events in the central nervous system.

Reflexes can be elicited from isolated parts of animals, so long as the preparation contains a sensory receptor for detecting the stimulus, a muscle or other effector which responds, and a functioning piece of the central nervous system connecting the sense organ and effector. Most of the studies of reflexes have been on "spinal" mammals, usually dogs or cats. The central nervous system is cut through so that most of the brain is separated from the spinal cord. Usually the transection is made just below the point where the nerves running to the diaphragm leave the brain, so the animal can still breath without assistance. Spinal animals no longer initiate behavior. They lie in one position, unable to stand or to walk. They move only when stimulated. The movements of a limb or of a single muscle are easily recorded by a lever tracing on a moving drum.

Serious work on spinal reflexes began at the turn of the century and culminated in the studies of Sir Charles Sherrington, summarized in 1906 in his book, *The Integrative Action of the Nervous System.* This book is a landmark in biology. It is still the best introduction to the study of reflexes and is also a model of the scientific approach to the study of behavior.

THE LAWS OF THE REFLEX

Sherrington's first aim was to discover and describe the important features common to different reflexes. He started by studying the flexion, or withdrawal, reflex. The reflex is elicited by a noxious stimulus on the surface of the body, such as a pinch, a prick, or a hot object applied to the footpad of a spinal dog. The response is the withdrawal or flexion of the leg. Since there is no pathway from the spinal cord to the brain, the stimulus cannot pain the animal. An electrical shock is a convenient stimulus because the intensity and duration of the shock can be easily controlled.

A weak shock given to the foot pad of the spinal dog does not cause a response. If the simulus intensity is raised by small steps, a point is abruptly reached where a response follows each stimulus. The stimulus intensity has reached the *threshold* for eliciting the reflex. One of the striking points about reflex behavior is how a slight stimulus elicits a powerful response. The central nervous system acts as an amplifier; the minute energy of the stimulus is magnified to produce a vigorous response. There is a pause between the stimulus and the first move-

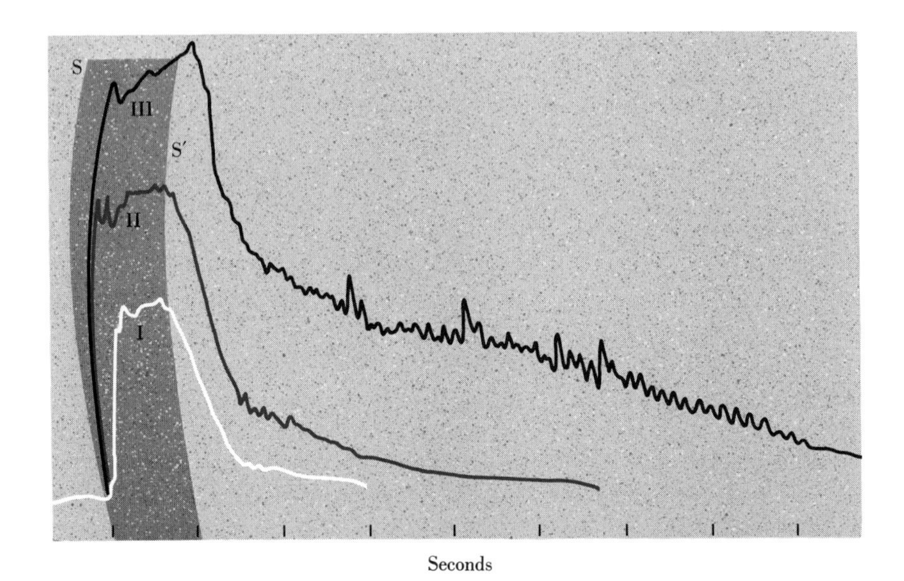

Fig. 2-1 *Records of the withdrawal of the leg of a spinal dog when a noxious stimulus was given to its foot pad. The stimulus starts at S and ends at S′. Stimulus intensity was raised from I to II to III. The stronger the stimulus, the more intense the response. Also notice the latency between the stimulus and the response, how the latency decreases when the stimulus strength is increased, and how the after-discharge is longer when the stimulus is stronger. (Adapted from C. S. Sherrington,* The Integrative Action of the Nervous System, *Yale University Press.)*

ment of the limb; this interval is the *reflex latency* (Figure 2-1). For the flexion reflex in the spinal dog, the minimum latency is about 22 milliseconds (1 millisecond = 0.001 second). The shortest reflex latencies occur when strong stimuli are given. The same reflex will have a longer latency when the stimulus is less intense.

A weak, minimum threshold stimulus to the footpad elicits a flexion of the foot or of the lower leg. A rise in the stimulus intensity produces a more powerful flexion of the lower leg. With a further increase in stimulus strength, the hip muscles are excited so that the upper part of the leg is flexed as well. The increase in the extent of the response with an increase in stimulus strength is called *irradiation.* The principle is familiar enough. A man who touches a hot stove withdraws the finger or perhaps the hand. If the stove is very hot, the entire arm is pulled back; if it is red hot, the victim springs backward, usually crying or cursing, and pulls the entire body away from present danger. The irradiation of protective reflexes is important for survival.

Irradiation is especially striking in animals with a transection of the midbrain. These animals assume a characteristic stiff posture with the legs rigidly extended; they can be propped into a standing position. A painful stimulus to the left hindleg causes a withdrawal of the leg. If the stimulus is sufficiently intense, the right foreleg is also flexed, so the animal assumes the position of the four limbs normally seen in walking or in running (Figure 2-2). The spinal cord performs the first steps in the behavior of moving the animal away. The posture is called a reflex figure. This is another example of how excitation can spread through the central nervous system when the stimulus intensity is increased.

A brief painful stimulus to the footpad causes withdrawal of the leg. After the stimulus is stopped, the leg only gradually returns to its normal position. The effects of the stimulus persist in some way within the animal long after the stimulus itself is over. The continuation of the response after the end of the stimulus is called *after-discharge* (see Figure 2-1).

In some reflexes the response is *rhythmic*. The classic example is the scratch reflex of the dog. An effective stimulus is a pointed cog wheel pulled over the skin, which mimics the sensory messages set up by a hopping flea. The scratch reflex can also be elicited by an electrical shock to the skin covering a saddle-shaped area on the dog's back (Figure 2-3). Even when the shock is given 500 times per second the response is the familiar rhythmic scratching motion by the hind leg. The leg moves back and forth four times per second. This shows

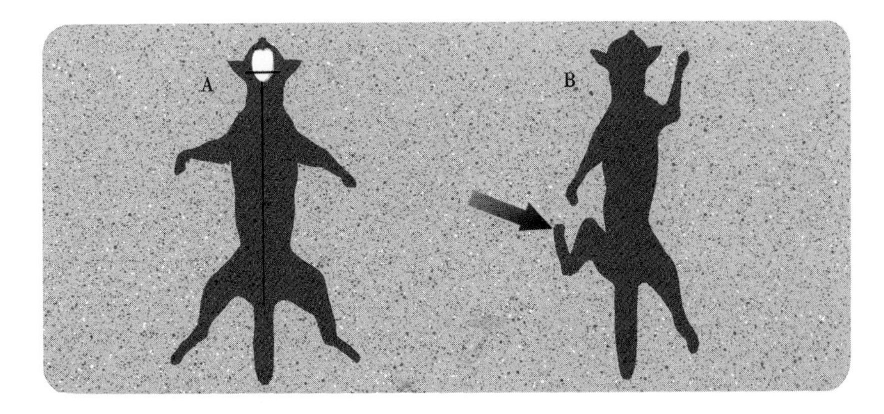

Fig. 2-2 *(Left). A spinal cat in its usual posture. (Right). The left hind paw has been given a noxious stimulus. The left hind paw is flexed and at the same time the right fore paw is extended. (Adapted from C. S. Sherrington,* The Integrative Action of the Nervous System, *Yale University Press.)*

Fig. 2-3 *The areas on the surface of the dog's body where stimulation elicits the scratch reflex. (Adapted from C. S. Sherrington,* The Integrative Action of the Nervous System, *Yale University Press.)*

that in a reflex the frequency of the response can be independent of the frequency of the stimulus. The scratching movements of the leg are directed toward the point being stimulated. The stimulus elicits the movements and also directs the movement toward the proper place. The directing of the movement toward the stimulus is called *local sign*. In the spinal dog, local sign is deficient. The animal scratches only in the general direction of the stimulus. Local sign does operate in the spinal dog to the extent that a stimulus on the right side elicits scratching by the right leg, and vice versa. Frequently the scratching rhythms of the right and left leg are different.

The scratch reflex can also be used to illustrate another important law of the reflex. The skin is stimulated with a weak, subthreshold stimulus. The weak stimulus is repeated eighteen times per second. The scratch reflex is elicited only after forty-four stimuli have been given. Stimuli are added up in the animal until a threshold is reached. This process is called *temporal summation*.

A second type of summation is produced by giving several subthreshold stimuli simultaneously at several different points on the skin. When given together, the stimuli elicit a response. This is *spatial summation*.

The experimenter can try to trick the animal by eliciting two reflexes simultaneously. For example, the scratch reflex is elicited and then a painful stimulus is given also. The animal never hesitates; scratching is stopped and the leg is flexed. If the painful stimulus is halted while the stimulus for scratching still goes on, scratching begins once again (Figure 2-4). The scratch and the flexion reflexes are *antagonistic*, that is, both are not carried on by the animal at the same time. The ability to choose between two stimuli, select the one most important to the survival of the animal, and then to respond to that one alone is a basic requisite for a central nervous system. As

Sherrington said, "The resulting singleness of action from moment to moment is a keystone in the construction of the individual whose unity it is the specific office of the central nervous system to perfect."

NEURONS AND REFLEXES

Once the general laws of reflexes were worked out, the next step was to find out how the behavior is produced by the spinal cord. Most of the first studies were done with the simplest spinal reflex, the stretch reflex. This is the reflex elicited by a hammer tap to the tendon. The tap on the tendon stretches out the muscle. The

Fig. 2-4 *(A). A recording of the scratching movements of the hind limb of the spinal dog. Bar S shows the stimulus duration. (B). A scratch reflex is elicited and then a noxious stimulus (Bar N) is given to the paw. Scratching promptly stops. When the noxious stimulus is discontinued, there is a delay and then scratching is resumed. Only one of these antagonistic reflexes can occur at one time. The time scale is in seconds. (Adapted from C. S. Sherrington,* The Integrative Action of the Nervous System, *Yale University Press.)*

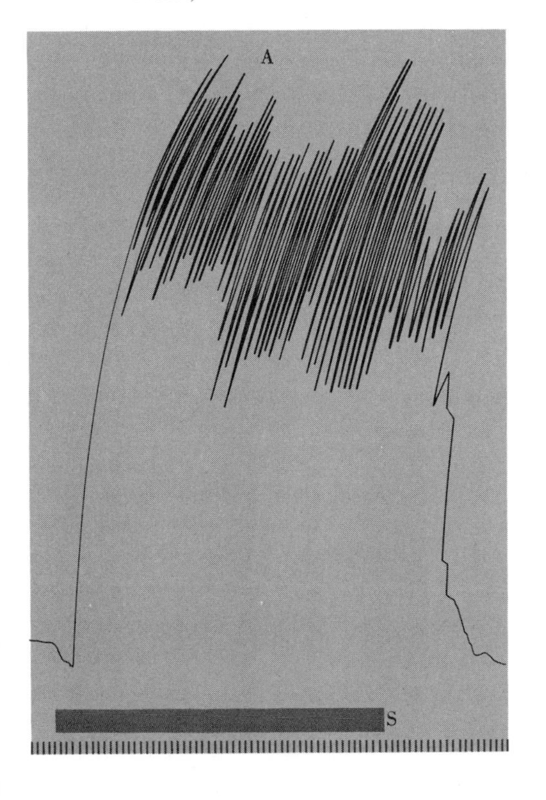

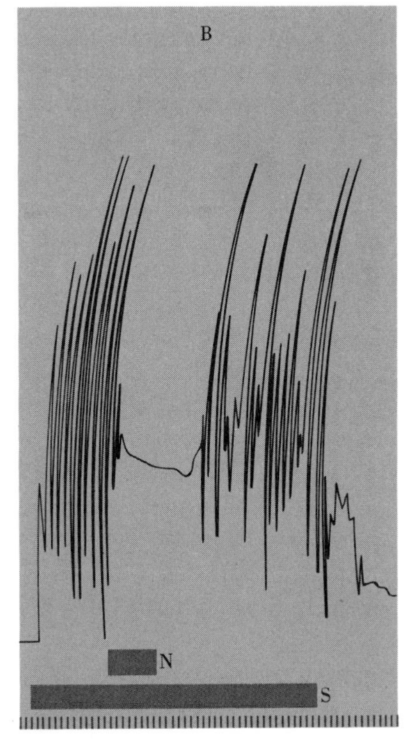

stretch stimulates a specialized structure, the stretch receptor or spindle organ, which is buried in the muscle. The reflex response to the pull on the stretch receptor is a quick twitch by the muscle. This reflex is the simplest because only two types of nerve cells are involved. The first type is the sensory neuron running from the stretch receptor to the spinal cord (Figure 2-5). All of the sensory neurons enter the spinal cord by way of the dorsal root. The cell bodies of the sensory, or afferent, neurons are in the dorsal root ganglion. The main axons from the stretch receptors are known as 1A afferents. When an afferent neuron enters the spinal cord, it branches repeatedly. One branch runs downward in the spinal cord and ends on the cell body of a motor neuron, or motoneuron, as it is usually called. The axon from the motoneuron leaves the spinal cord in the ventral root, along with the axons of all of the other efferent fibers which conduct impulses to muscles and glands.

The junction between the 1A afferent and the motoneuron is a specialized region called a synapse. There is a gap of about 200 angstrom units between the terminal of the 1A afferent and the membrane of the motoneuron. The critical event in the reflex is the passage of excitation from the sensory neuron to the motor nerve by crossing the synapse. In the stretch reflex there is only a single synapse in the central nervous system to be crossed, so it is a monosynaptic reflex. All other reflexes involve two or more central synapses and are known as polysynaptic reflexes. We shall now look, in turn, at each step in the monosynaptic reflex.

Fig. 2-5 *A diagram of the anatomy of the stretch reflex, a monosynaptic reflex arc.*

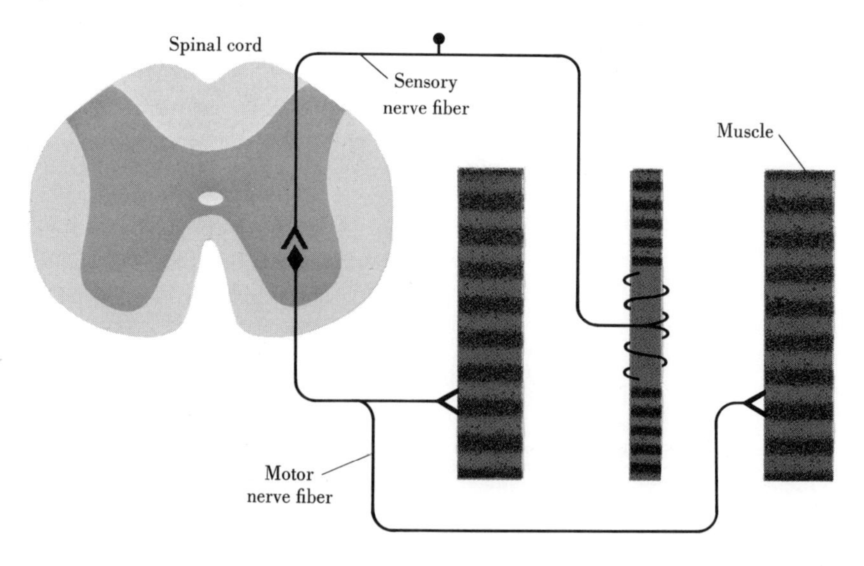

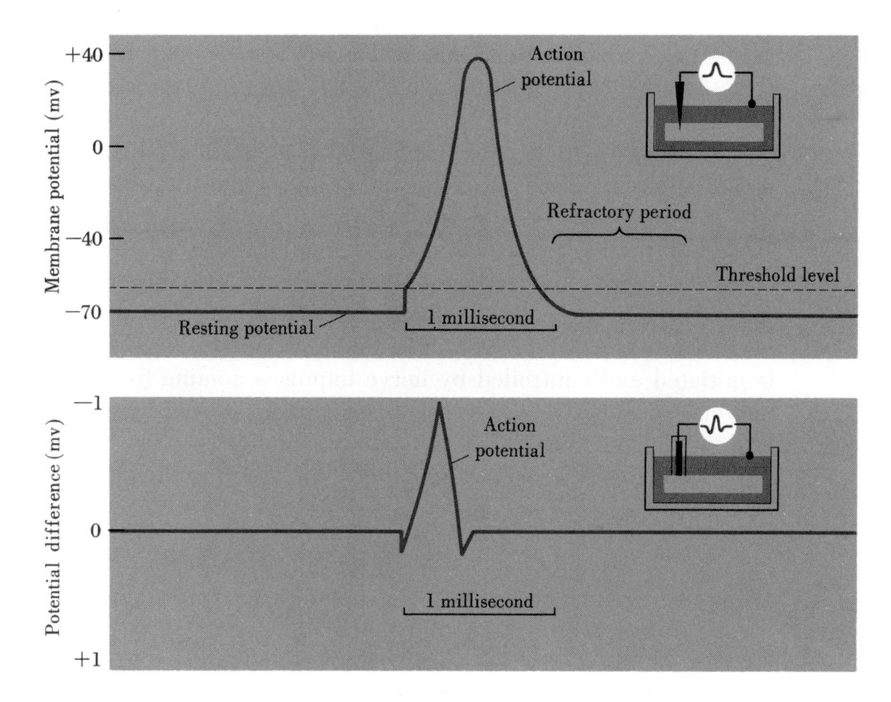

Fig. 2-6 (Upper). The action potential recorded by measuring the voltage difference between a microelectrode inserted through the nerve cell membrane and a large electrode in the extracellular solution. (Lower). The action potential as recorded between a fine electrode on the surface of a nerve cell and a large electrode in the solution.

AXONS The axons of all of the neurons in the nervous system work in the same way. The cell membrane of a resting neuron is charged with electricity. The inside of the cell is 70 to 100 millivolts (1 millivolt = 0.001 volt) negative compared to the solution outside of the cell. This is the resting potential of the cell membrane. If at one point on the membrane the potential is abruptly decreased by 10 millivolts, so that the potential on the inside of the cell changes from −70 to −60 millivolts, a threshold is reached and there is a profound, but transitory, change in the properties of the cell membrane. The change in the cell membrane causes a rapid shift in the potential and for an instant the interior of the cell becomes positive compared with the outside (Figure 2-6). The potential quickly returns to the resting level. The whole sequence is over in less than one millisecond. This transitory alteration in the charge on the cell membrane is called the action potential or the spike.

When one point on an axon is stimulated, the action potential travels in both directions away from this point. The rate of conduction varies depending on the axon, ranging from more than 100 meters per second in the thickest motor axons to a few tenths of a meter per second in small, thin axons.

After an action potential has been generated by the nerve cell membrane, there is a brief period during which the axon cannot be re-excited, no matter how intense the stimulus. This interval is the refractory period; it lasts for 0.4 to 2.0 milliseconds, depending on the axon. Therefore, the action potential is always followed by a pause during which the nerve cannot conduct again. Every sensation is carried into the central nervous system by nerve fibers. Every motion is initiated and controlled by nerve impulses coming from the central nervous system. These messages are all transmitted by a code which has only a single character, the action potential.

From our standpoint, the important features of the action potential are:

1. The action potential is set up when one point on the cell membrane is depolarized to the threshold level. Threshold is 10 to 15 millivolts less than the resting potential. Once threshold is reached the size of the action potential is independent of the strength of the stimulus. The action potential is "all or none": it is present or not present, there are no gradations.

2. Once an action potential is set up, it is conducted over the entire axon and cell body. Each part of the membrane generates its own action potential, so the spike sweeps over the axon without changing in size. If the axon branches, the action potential is conducted without diminution into both branches.

3. The axon is refractory to stimulation for a short time after an action potential has passed. The action potential is always followed by an interval before the next one can be set up.

The action potential is an electrical event generated by a change in the properties of the neuron cell membrane. The action potential can be measured in large nerve cells by piercing the membrane with a fine glass capillary tube. The capillary is filled with concentrated salt solution, so it conducts electricity. The tip diameter must be less than one micron to penetrate the cell membrane without producing irreparable damage. The electrical potential between the intracellular microelectrode and a second electrode in the solution outside of the cell is measured (Figure 2-6).

The action potential can also be recorded by placing a fine wire close to the outside of the axon, and recording the potential difference between the extracellular electrode and a second electrode placed away from the axon (Figure 2-6). The extracellular recording does not

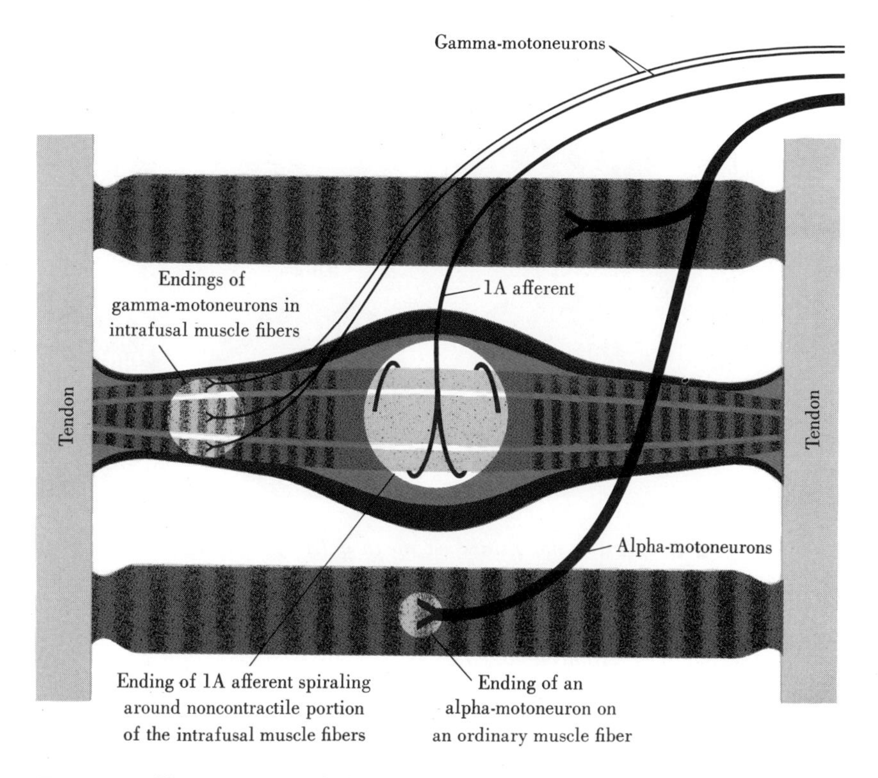

Fig. 2-7 *The anatomy of the spindle organ and of some of the adjacent ordinary muscle fibers. (After Baker,* Quarterly Journal of Microscopical Science.*)*

give any information about the absolute size of the change in potential across the membrane; it does give a clear indication whenever an action potential is conducted over the cell.

THE STRETCH RECEPTOR The receptor that senses the stretching of a muscle is the spindle organ (Figure 2-7). The spindle consists of a capsule containing a number of small muscle fibers, the intrafusal fibers. The central portions of the intrafusal fibers are not striated like normal muscle and are elastic rather than contractile. The ending of a 1A afferent neuron is wrapped around the central portion of the intrafusal fiber. The 1A afferent fiber runs from the stretch receptor to the spinal cord.

A single spindle organ with a length of the sensory axon can be dissected free from a muscle. When the spindle organ is stretched out with a small weight, extracellular action potentials are recorded from

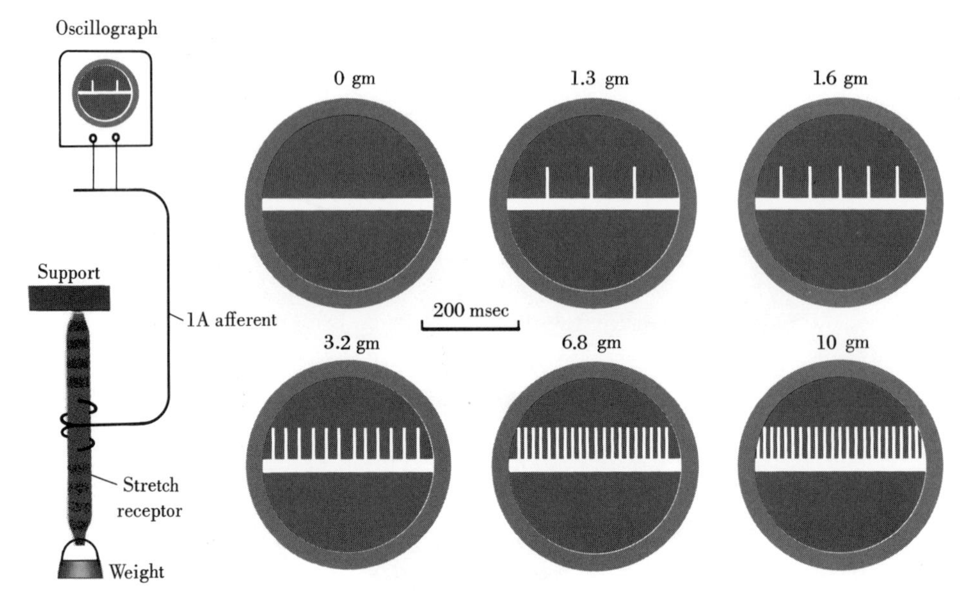

Fig. 2-8 *Action potentials set up in a 1A afferent nerve fiber when different weights are used to stretch out the spindle organ. Each action potential appears as a single vertical line because of the slow time scale used in this recording (After Hunt and Kuffler,* Journal of Physiology; *and Kuffler, Hunt, and Quilliam,* Journal of Neurophysiology.*)*

the axon (Figure 2-8). The frequency at which action potentials are generated by the organ depends on the weight: the heavier the weight, the higher the frequency of the action potentials. When the weight is made ten times heavier, the frequency of the action potentials doubles. When the weight is one hundred times heavier, the frequency of the action potential triples. As with most sense organs, the rate at which nerve impulses are generated varies with the logarithm of the stimulus intensity (Figure 2-9).

So far, we have been concerned only with the rate at which nerve impulses are generated in the first second after the receptor is stretched. If the weight is left pulling on the receptor, the frequency of the action potentials declines from the high initial value and levels off at a lower rate. The decrease in the rate of firing during a steady stimulus is called adaptation. All sense organs adapt to some extent at least.

The spindle organ is placed so that it runs parallel to the ordinary muscle fibers. The intrafusal muscle fibers extend from the tendon at one end of the muscle to the tendon at the other end (Figure 2-10). The anatomical relation between the spindle organ and the rest of the muscle must be kept in mind to understand the sensory system. If the entire muscle is pulled out, the spindle organs are lengthened and nerve impulses appear at a higher frequency in the 1A afferents.

The ordinary muscle fibers are innervated by the axons from large motoneurons whose cell bodies lie in the spinal cord. They are

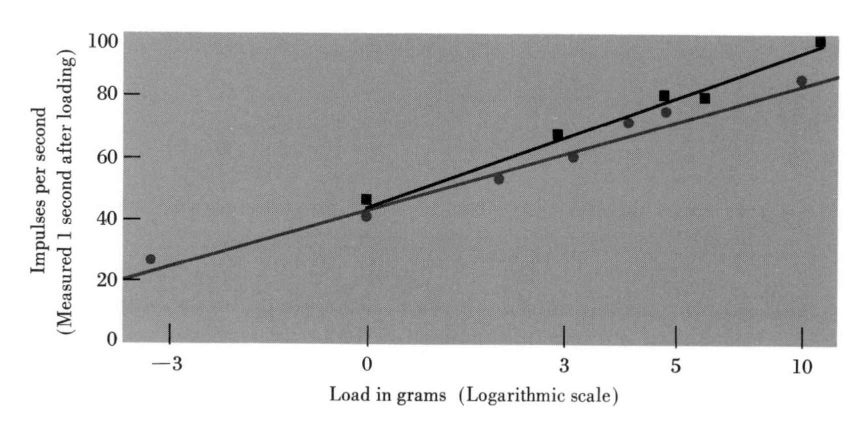

Fig. 2-9 *The relation between the weight used to stretch out a spindle organ and the frequency of action potentials in the 1A afferents. Two separate experiments are shown. Notice how reproducible the points are from one time to the next. (After Matthews,* Journal of Physiology.*)*

Fig. 2-10 *Electrical recording from a motor neuron in the spinal cord. (Upper). A microelectrode is advanced through the cord until the motor neuron cell body is penetrated, which is shown by the sudden appearance of the resting potential. When the ventral root is stimulated (colored dot), an action potential is conducted up the axon back to the cell body. (Lower). Stimuli of increasing intensity are given to 1A afferents in the dorsal root. The higher the intensity the more 1A afferents are excited. An EPSP is set up in the motoneuron; if the EPSP reaches the threshold an action potential is generated. (After Eccles, Harvey Lectures, 1955–1956, Academic Press.)*

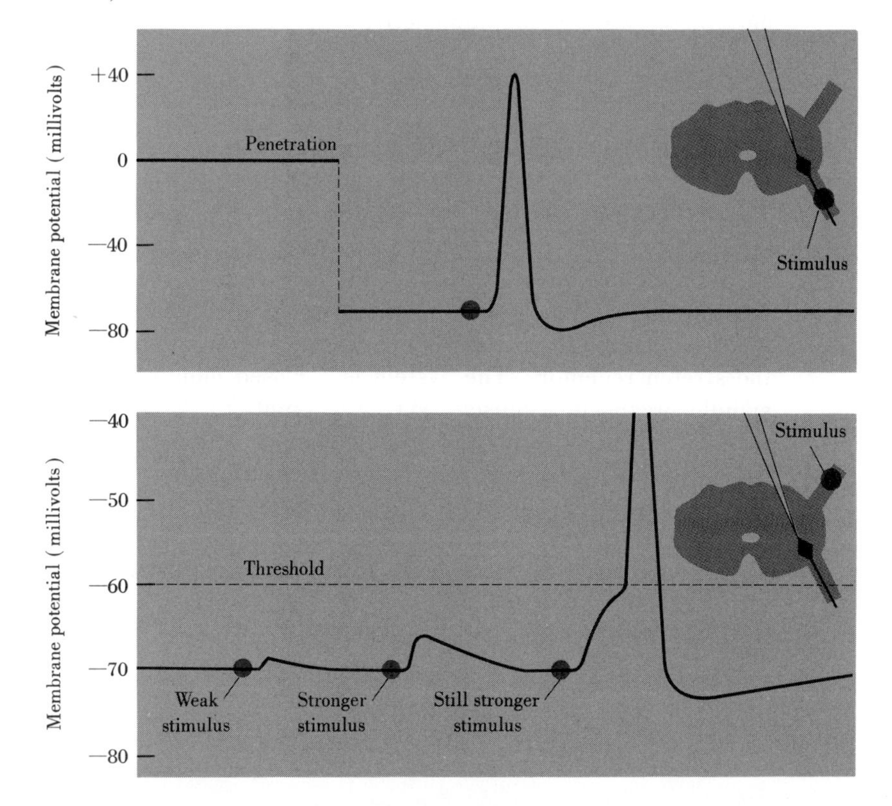

known as alpha-motoneurons. Each time an action potential is generated in the cell body of an alpha-motoneuron, the spike is conducted down the axon and out to the muscle. The tension exerted by the muscle goes up when alpha-motoneurons fire at a faster rate.

The intrafusal muscle fibers of the spindle organ are driven by certain motoneurons with small cell bodies in the spinal cord. These are called gamma-motoneurons. If the ventral root of the spinal cord is lightly clamped, the pressure blocks action potentials in the alpha-motoneurons, while the gamma-motoneurons still conduct. Stimulation of the gamma-motoneurons causes the intrafusal muscle fibers of the stretch receptor to contract. The intrafusal fibers are small and make up only a trivial portion of the mass of the muscle, so the length of the muscle does not change. Since the muscle as a whole remains at its original length, the elastic central part of the intrafusal muscle fibers is pulled out when the striated parts contract. The ending of the sensory nerve is stretched, and the rate of firing in the 1A afferents increases, just as if the entire muscle had been pulled out. In the intact animal the rate of firing in the axons from the spindle organ always depends on two factors: (1) the stretch on the muscle and (2) the rate of firing of the gamma-motoneurons. The rate of firing in the 1A afferents goes up either when the muscle is stretched or when the gamma-motoneurons discharge more rapidly. The role of the gamma system in regulating movements will be taken up shortly.

THE SYNAPSES BETWEEN 1A AFFERENTS AND ALPHA-MOTONEURONS

The 1A afferents enter the spinal cord in the dorsal root and then branch a number of times. Some branches ascend the spinal cord and run to the brain; other branches go to other segments of the spinal cord. Among the branches that remain in the same segment of the spinal cord, some synapse with alpha-motoneurons. The motoneurons run to the muscle that contains the stretch receptors. The system is a closed loop, running from the spindle organs in a muscle, via 1A afferents to the spinal cord, and then via alpha-motoneurons back to ordinary fibers in the same muscle. The physiology of the synapses on the motoneurons has been intensively studied during the last fifteen years, particularly by Sir John Eccles and his coworkers in Australia. They showed that the cell body of an alpha-motoneuron in the spinal cord of a cat can be impaled with a glass capillary microelectrode. The experimenter knows that the microelectrode tip has penetrated into a cell when a −70 millivolts resting potential is suddenly recorded. The next step is to stimulate the ventral root. The ventral root contains only motor and other efferent fibers. The stimulus sets up an action potential in the motoneuron axons. The action potentials are conducted out toward the muscles and also back into the cell bodies in the spinal cord. If the impaled cell generates an action potential after the ventral root is stimulated, the microelectrode must be in a motoneuron (Figure 2-10). The action potential is not conducted from the motoneuron cell body to the sensory fiber because the synapse conducts in the opposite direction only.

EXCITATORY POSTSYNAPTIC POTENTIALS

Suppose the microelectrode is successfully inserted into a motoneuron. The next step is to gently stretch the muscle; the stretch is so gentle that there is no reflex response. But action potentials are generated in a few of the 1A afferents. The action potentials travel into the spinal cord and produce a small transient decrease in the membrane potential of the motoneuron. The membrane recovers to the resting potential in 10 milliseconds. The transient change recorded in the motoneuron is called an excitatory postsynaptic potential, or EPSP.

An EPSP arises in the following way. The action potential travels from the stretch receptor to the terminal of the 1A afferent. It causes the terminal to release a tiny amount of a chemical transmitter (the identity of the transmitter is not known). The transmitter diffuses across the 200 angstrom unit gap between the terminal and the motoneuron membrane. The transmitter changes the properties of the motoneuron membrane, so the motoneuron depolarizes slightly. The effects of the transmitter are short-lived. Probably the transmitter is rapidly destroyed by an enzyme. Synaptic transmission takes time, the minimum delay at a synapse of this type is 0.4 milliseconds.

What happens if the muscle is stretched further? More of the spindle organs in the muscle are excited and more of the 1A afferents conduct impulses into the cord. Each motoneuron synapses with many 1A afferents, so now a number of EPSPs are simultaneously set up on the cell body. The EPSPs add together and decrease the potential on the membrane. If ten to fifteen EPSPs are generated at the same time the motoneuron is depolarized to the threshold level. An action potential is set up which travels out to the muscle (Figure 2-10). The threshold for the reflex was reached by stimulating more sense organs at the same time, that is, by spatial summation. The spatial summation is accomplished by adding together EPSPs on the motoneuron cell body.

TEMPORAL SUMMATION Motoneurons can also be stimulated by temporal summation. A spindle organ is pulled out so that it generates sensory impulses at a high frequency. Each action potential in the 1A afferent sets up an EPSP on the motoneurons. Before one EPSP has time to decay, a second EPSP is added. In this fashion a whole series of EPSPs stand on each others backs until threshold is reached and the motoneuron fires an action potential (Figure 2-11).

The key to understanding the behavior of motoneurons, and of many other types of cell in the central nervous system, is that they can add together EPSPs arriving within a few milliseconds of one another. The cell body of a motoneuron is covered with synapses from 1A afferents, from other neurons in the spinal cord, and from axons coming from the brain. The motoneuron is always summing the influences coming in from this large number of channels (Figure 2-12).

INHIBITORY POSTSYNAPTIC POTENTIALS The motoneuron has inhibitory synapses as well as excitatory. So far, we have only considered the reflex activity of the muscle which was stretched. The general plan of vertebrate limb musculature is that each muscle is opposed by an antagonist, which moves the limb in the opposite direction. Experiments on spinal animals show that when a muscle is stretched, the antagonistic muscle relaxes. The mechanism for the relaxation can be understood from experiments in which a microelectrode is in a motoneuron cell body and the antagonistic muscle is suddenly stretched. After a brief delay, the interior of the motoneuron becomes more negative than the resting potential; the neuron hyperpolarizes. After about 7 milliseconds, the potential returns to the resting level (Figure 2-13). The transitory hyperpolarization is an inhibitory postsynaptic potential, or IPSP.

Why is the IPSP inhibitory? Remember that the motoneuron fires when its membrane potential is decreased from −70 millivolts to −60 millivolts. IPSPs increase the membrane potential, so the cell is further away from threshold. More EPSPs would have to be generated at the same time to reach threshold and to fire the cell. In an intact animal the motoneurons are always being bombarded with both excitatory and inhibitory synaptic inputs. The behavior of the cell is always determined by the sum of the EPSPs and of the IPSPs. The adding together of synaptic influences is the basis for the integrative action of the nervous system.

The anatomy of the circuit for generating IPSPs on antagonistic motoneurons is somewhat more roundabout than the direct excitatory

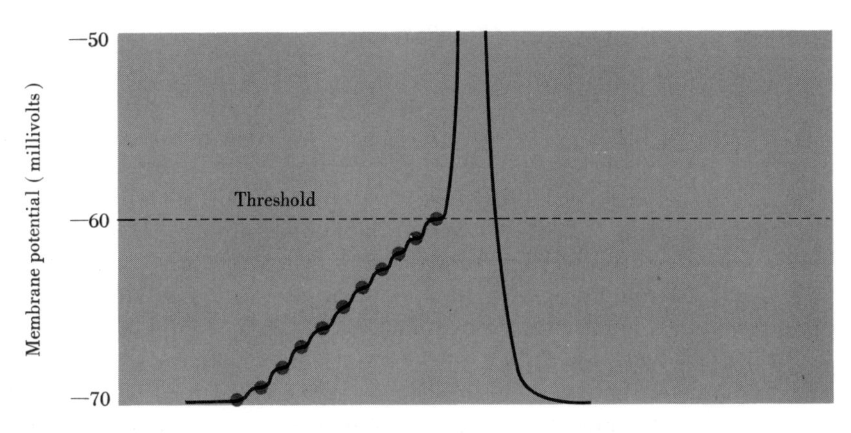

Fig. 2-11 *An intracellular recording from a motoneuron. A few 1A afferents are stimulated repeatedly at short intervals. The EPSPs summate and bring the membrane potential of the motor neuron to threshold.*

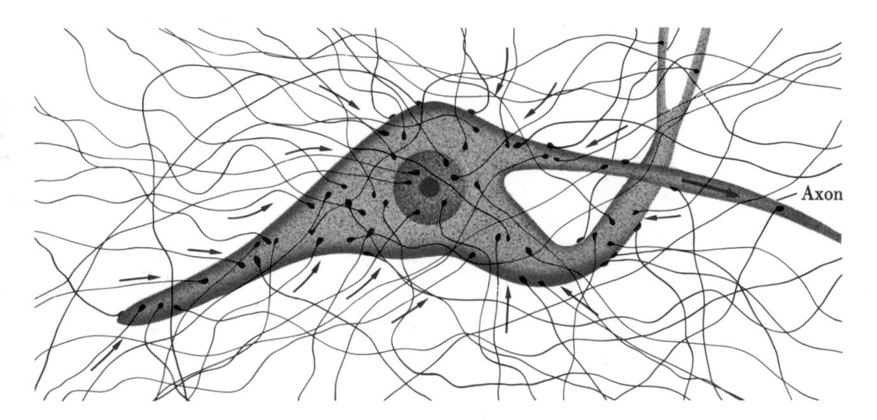

Fig. 2-12 *The cell body of a spinal motoneuron, giving some idea of the number of synapses from afferent fibers that converge on each motoneuron. (Redrawn from "How cells communicate" by B. Katz, Copyright © 1961 by Scientific American, Inc. All rights reserved.)*

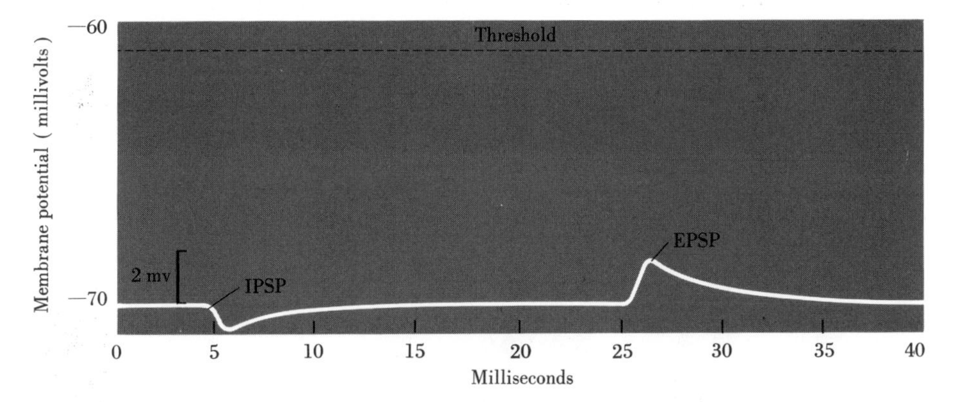

Fig. 2-13 *An inhibitory post synaptic potential (IPSP) and an EPSP recorded from a motor neuron cell body (After Araki, Eccles, and Ito,* Journal of Physiology.*)*

path. One of the branches from a 1A afferent synapses with a neuron whose cell body and axon are entirely within the central nervous system. Cells like this are called interneurons. This particular interneuron runs a short distance in the spinal cord and then synapses with a motoneuron of the antagonistic muscle (Figure 2-14). When the muscle containing the spindle organ is stretched, the 1A afferents conduct impulses into the spinal cord. Some of the branches from the 1A afferents set up action potentials in the interneurons. The EPSP set up in the interneuron always reaches threshold without requiring spatial or temporal summation. When the action potential reaches the

Fig. 2-14 *The most direct nerve pathway between a stretch receptor and a motor neuron running to the antagonist muscle.*

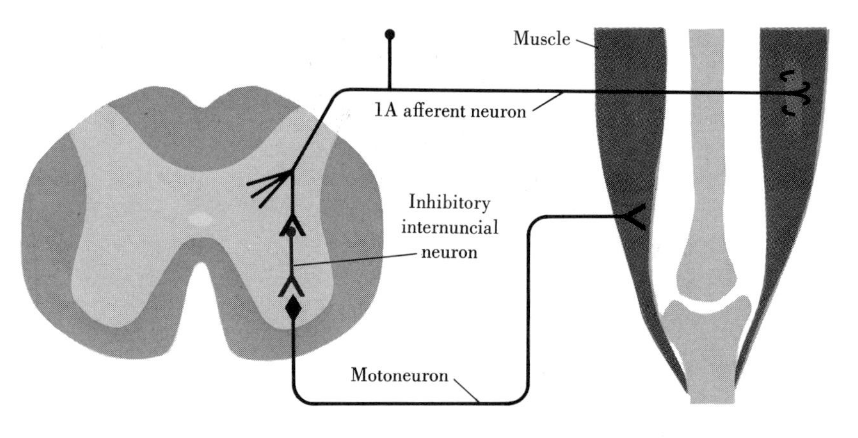

Fig. 2-15 *A polysynaptic reflex arc between sensory neurons in the skin and motor neurons.*

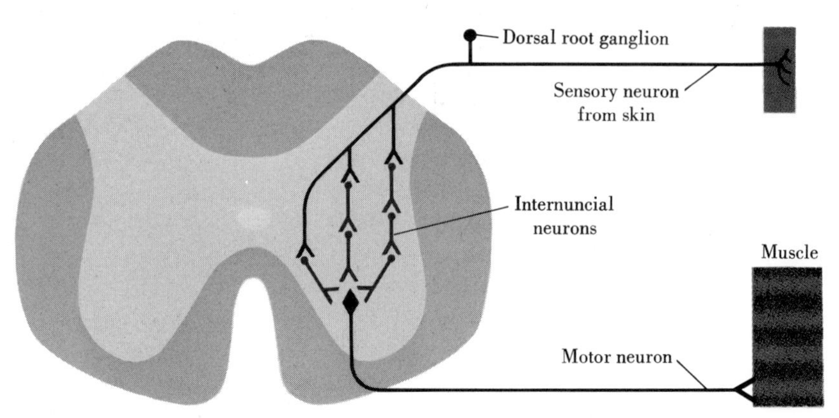

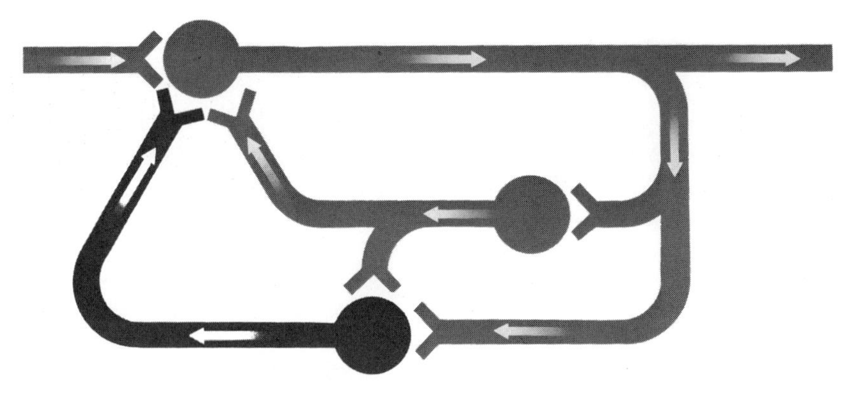

Fig. 2-16 *A closed chain of interneurons (After Lorente de No,* Journal of Neurophysiology.*)*

terminal of the interneuron, it causes the release of a transmitter which acts on the motoneuron membrane to produce the IPSP. One transmitter causes an IPSP. Apparently each individual neuron can make and release only one transmitter chemical.

THE FLEXION REFLEX In the flexion reflex the shortest path between the sensory neuron from pain receptors and the motoneuron is by way of an interneuron (Figure 2-15). There are also longer pathways between the afferent axons and the motoneurons, involving several or even dozens of interneurons. The delay at each synapse in the chain of neurons is about 0.5 milliseconds. With more synapses in the pathway, a longer time elapses between the stimulus and the conclusion of the motor response. The existence of long pathways with many interneurons is one of the mechanisms responsible for after-discharge. After-discharge also occurs if the sense organ continues to fire after the stimulus is over, as in the flexion reflex.

The after-discharge of some reflexes is very long. The receptor does not continue to fire and an interneuron chain would have to be very long to account for the after-discharge. The excitation set up by the stimulus may be traveling around and around closed chains of interneurons (Figure 2-16). Impulses might travel a circular path for many minutes. At present all of the evidence for persistent excitation in circular pathways in mammals is anatomical. The idea of a reverberatory loop of neurons has been important in speculation about the neural changes in learning (see Chapter 5).

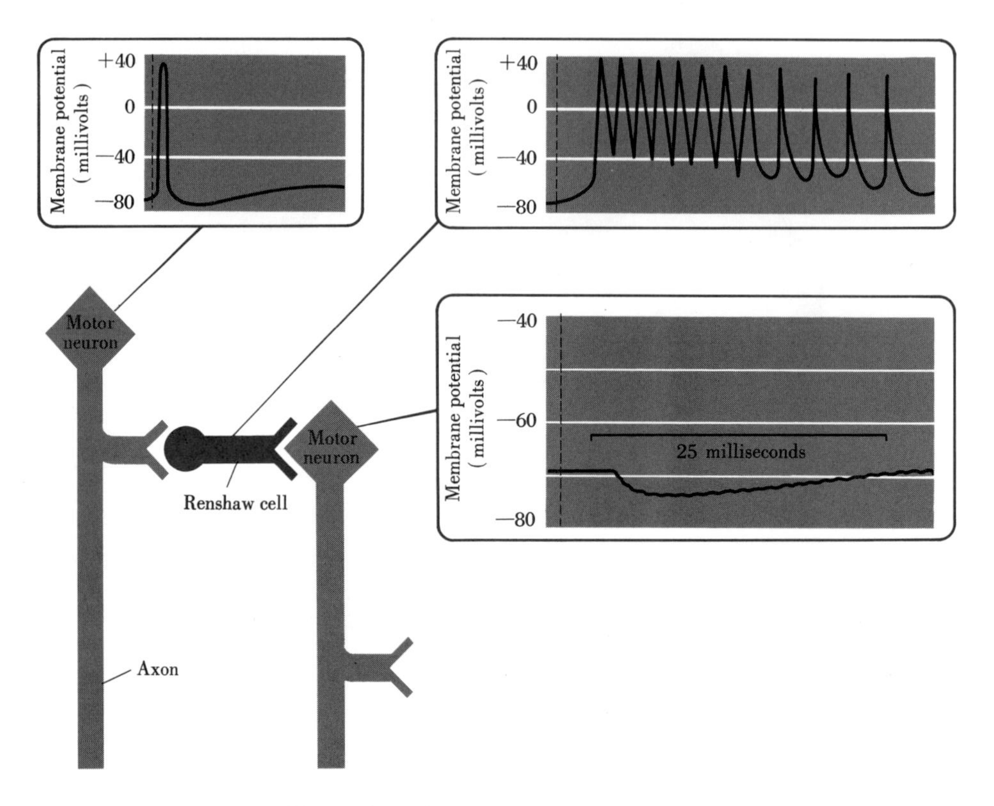

Fig. 2-17 *The circuit formed by a motor neuron, a Renshaw cell, and another motor neuron running to the same muscle. An action potential in the first motor neuron causes repetitive firing of the Renshaw cell, which in turn sets up a long series of IPSPs in the second motor neuron (After Eccles,* Physiology of Synapses, *Academic Press Inc.)*

RECURRENT INHIBITION Every muscle is innervated by a number of motoneurons. Each of the motoneurons runs to only some of the fibers in the muscle. The cell bodies of all of the motoneurons going to a muscle lie close to one another in the spinal cord; the group is called a pool. Imagine that a microelectrode is inserted into one of the motoneurons of a pool and a reflex involving the pool is elicited. Suppose that the particular motoneuron we are observing is not excited, even though other motoneurons in the pool do generate action potentials. The cell we are studying still develops a hyperpolarization lasting from 25 to 200 milliseconds (Figure 2-17). The circuit of neurons responsible for the hyperpolarization is shown in Figure 2-17. The axon of each motoneuron branches before it leaves the spinal cord. The branch synapses with an interneuron called a Renshaw cell. When the motoneuron is excited, the action potential is conducted into the branch leading to the Renshaw cell. The terminal of the motoneuron then releases a minute amount of the transmitter chemical, acetylcholine. The acetylcholine sets up a large EPSP on the cell body of the Renshaw cell which begins to fire nerve impulses. The EPSP set up on the Renshaw cell is long-lasting, probably because the acetylcholine released by the motoneuron terminal is destroyed only slowly. Consequently, the Renshaw cell generates a long burst of impulses. The Renshaw cell runs back to the same motoneuron pool. The synapse between the axon of the Renshaw cell and the motoneuron cell body is inhibitory. When the Renshaw cell fires repetitively, a whole series of IPSPs are set up on the cell body of the motoneuron. The IPSPs sum to give the long-lasting hyperpolarization.

The circuit between the motoneurons and the Renshaw cell indicates that whenever some of the motoneurons in the pool are stimulated, all of the motoneurons in the pool will be partially inhibited for the next 25 to 200 milliseconds. The entire pool of motoneurons will recover normal excitability at about the same time and will be ready to fire together. The recurrent inhibitory system favors the firing of all of the neurons in the pool as a group. Recurrent inhibition is found at all levels of the central nervous system. It probably is an important mechanism for coordinating the activity of groups of neurons that serve a common function.

THE GAMMA-EFFERENT SYSTEM

The picture presented so far is the classic view of the polysynaptic reflex arc. The scheme completely ignores the presence of the gamma-motoneurons, which innervate the intrafusal muscle fibers of the stretch receptor. The final step in understanding spinal reflexes is to put the gamma-motoneurons into the picture. The relation between excitation of the stretch receptor, the length of the muscle, and the rate of firing of the gamma-motoneurons is summarized in Figure 2-18. When the gamma-motoneurons are stimulated, the intrafusal muscle fibers contract. The sensory endings are stretched and impulses are generated in the 1A afferents. However, if the whole muscle shortens, the intrafusal muscle fibers simply contract to a shorter length, and the sensory ending is not stretched.

Now think of the situation in the intact animal. Suppose that the alpha-motoneurons are stimulated. The muscle fibers are excited and they exert tension. The distance the muscle actually moves depends on the load it must pull. Stimulation of the alpha-motoneurons tells

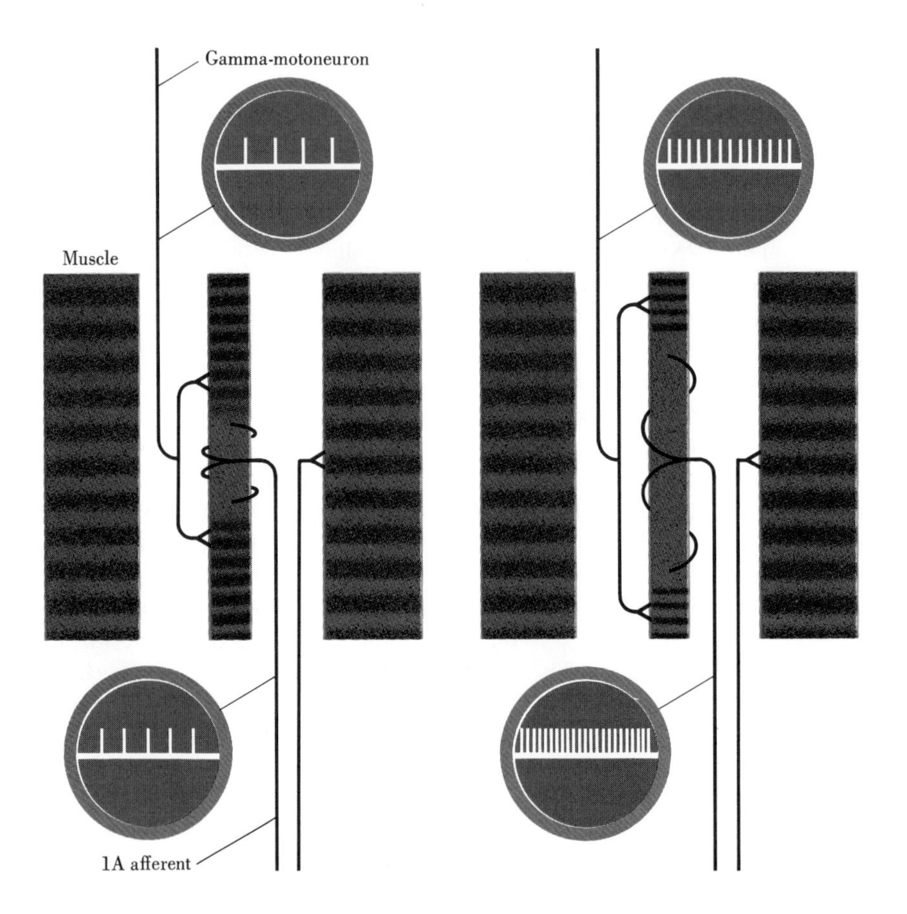

the muscle how hard to pull. Now suppose that the gamma-motoneurons are stimulated instead. The intrafusal muscle fibers contract and there is an increased rate of firing by the 1A afferents. The alpha-motoneurons are excited by the 1A afferents and the entire muscle begins to shorten. The muscle shortens until the increased pull on the sensory ending from the contraction of the intrafusal fibers is matched by the decreased pull resulting from the shortening of the entire muscle. In other words, the rate of gamma-motoneuron firing tells the muscle how far to shorten. The great advantage to having the gamma system is that it instructs the muscle how far to move, not merely how hard to pull.

The gamma-motoneurons are driven by impulses from higher levels of the central nervous system and by sensory messages from the body surface. As a rule, the gamma-motoneurons start every movement. Even when pain fibers are stimulated, the gamma-motoneurons are

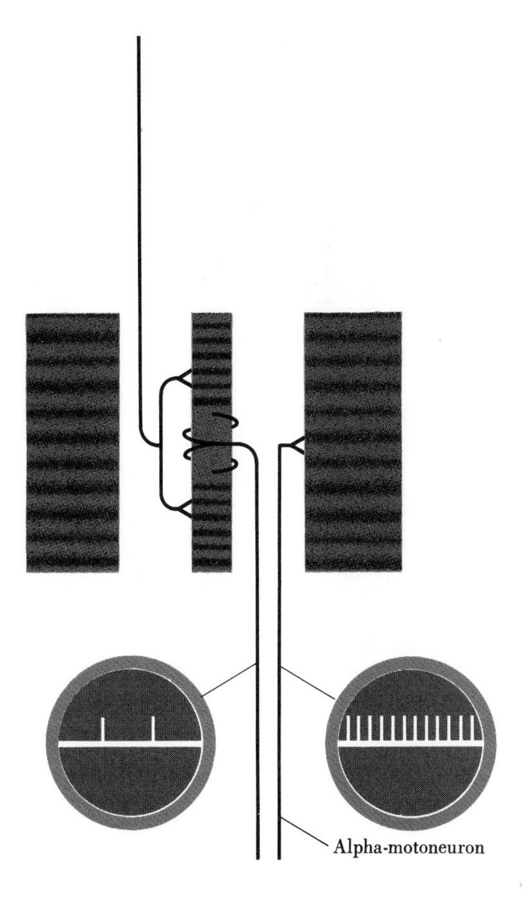

Fig. 2-18 *The relations between muscle length, the excitation of the stretch receptors, and the activity of the gamma-motoneurons. (Left and center). An increase in the rate of firing of the gamma-motorneurons causes the intrafusal muscle fibers of the spindle organ to contract further, pulling out the ending of the 1A afferent, and thereby causing an increased rate of 1A discharge. (Right). The firing of alpha-motorneurons causes the muscle to shorten. There is less pull on the stretch receptor, so the rate firing by the 1A afferent is low.*

activated first and begin to fire before the alpha-motoneurons. The action potentials from the gamma-motoneurons cause the intrafusal muscle fibers to contract. The sensory ending in the spindle organ is pulled out and a burst of impulses is set up in the 1A afferent (Figure 2-19). The alpha-motoneurons are activated both by the interneurons excited by the pain afferents and by the 1A afferents. The alpha-motoneurons fire and the muscle contracts.

The contraction of the muscle has two effects. First, the limb is moved, which usually eliminates the painful stimulus, and the rate of firing in the pain receptors begins to go down. Second, the contraction of the muscle allows the intrafusal muscle fibers to shorten, lessening the pull on the ending of the stretch receptor, and the rate of firing in the 1A afferents goes down. Both effects decrease the excitation of the alpha-motoneurons and halt the contraction of the muscle.

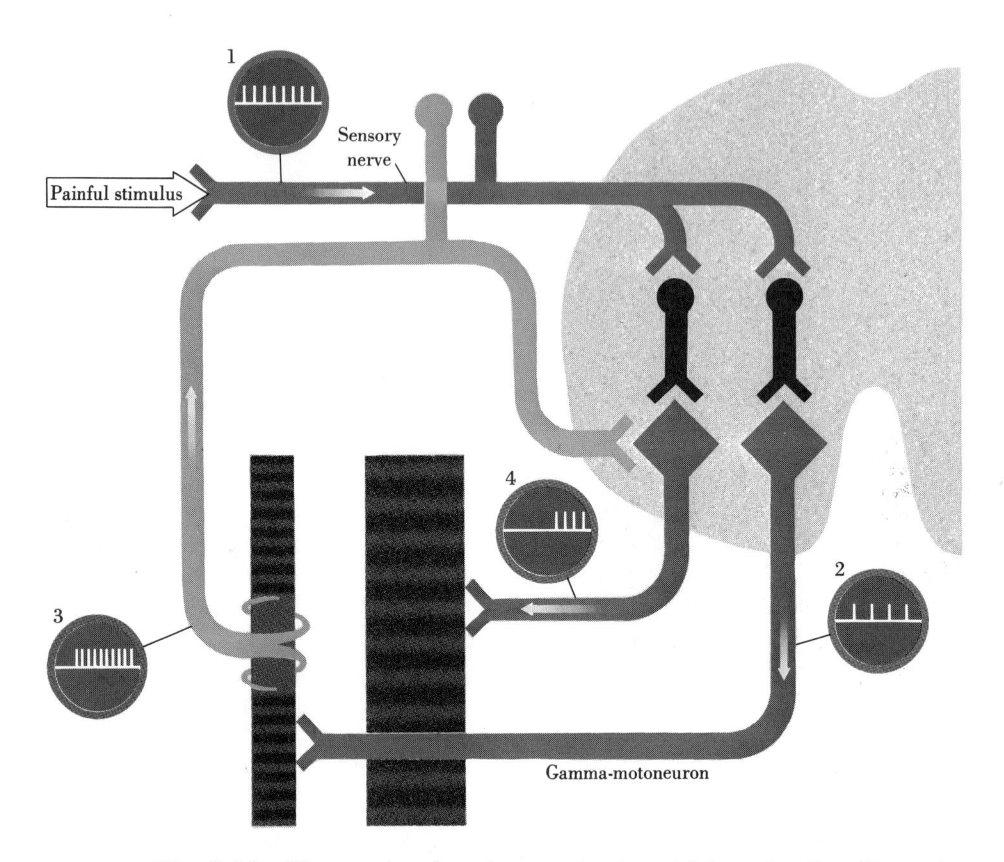

Fig. 2-19 *The usual order of events in the withdrawal reflex. The painful stimulus sets up action potentials in the sensory nerve (1). The excitation of internuncials in the spinal cord leads to an increased rate of firing in the gamma-motoneurons (2), so that the intrafusal muscle fibers contract. The contraction pulls out the stretch receptor and causes an increased firing in the 1A afferents (3). Action potentials are therefore generated in the alpha-motoneurons (4) which cause the muscle to contract and to move the limb away from the noxious stimulus.*

SYNAPSES, CIRCUITS, AND BEHAVIOR

There are two essential steps in the analysis of reflex behavior. The first step is anatomical. To understand a reflex, we must know which neurons synapse with one another. We must be able to draw a diagram of the circuit. This is a difficult job even for the shortest reflex chains in the spinal cord, and it is much more difficult when the central nervous system is viewed as a whole.

In man, there are approximately 3×10^6 sensory axons entering the central nervous system. Each of the sensory axons fires in response to one type of stimulus at one point on, or in, the body. There are $1 - 2 \times 10^{10}$ interneurons. The interneurons connect with one another and some run to the 150,000 motoneurons. The motoneurons carry all of the output from the nervous system. The small number of motoneurons compared to sensory fibers emphasizes one aspect of the work of the nervous system. The myriad messages coming in the sensory channels are analyzed and weighed; and produce an output which is a coherent pattern of movement of the fibers in a muscle, the muscles on a limb, and the limbs of the body. As Sherrington emphasized, the motoneurons are the final common path out of the nervous system. The integrative action of the nervous system is the transformation of diverse and even conflicting sensory messages into a unified course of motor action.

Nerve tracts can be followed in stained sections of the nervous system. If the cell bodies of a group of neurons are destroyed, the axons begin to degenerate. Degenerating axons have a special affinity for certain stains. This gives a useful method for tracing the axons running from a group of cell bodies. Circuits in the nervous system can also be traced by electrical techniques. One point is stimulated and recordings are made at different sites until a place is found where an action potential always appears following the stimulus. These methods are quite good for following large groups of axons which run as a tract through the nervous system, but they are much more difficult to use effectively when small numbers of fibers are each going their own way. There are many important unsolved problems in the organization of circuits in the central nervous system which can be solved by present techniques, but we also need new methods for working out the finer microanatomy.

The second aspect in the analysis of the reflex is the mode of operation of the synapses at the different points around the circuit. There are both excitatory and inhibitory synapses. We have seen examples of three types of excitatory synapse: (1) Relay. The synapse between the 1A afferent and the inhibitory interneuron which runs to antagonistic motoneurons is a simple relay station. Every impulse arriving at the presynaptic terminals is transmitted to the interneuron. (2) Repetitive. The synapse between the motoneuron and the Renshaw cell gives a repetitive burst of action potentials in the postsynaptic fiber when a single impulse comes in the presynaptic ending. (3) Summing. The motoneuron operates by summing together EPSPs and IPSPs; it can never be activated by a single impulse arriving on one presynaptic fiber.

There is yet another type of synapse. This is an inhibitory synapse on the terminal of an excitatory neuron. Activation of this inhibitory synapse decreases the amount of transmitter released when the interneuron is stimulated. Therefore, the interneuron generates a smaller

EPSP on the neuron it innervates. This is presynaptic inhibition. The variety of synapses comes in part from the use of specific chemicals in transmission between cells. Chemical transmission gives a wider range of synaptic types and also gives ways for the function of the synapse to change by varying the amount of released chemical.

The examples show that a reflex pathway cannot be understood merely by knowing where neurons run and where synapses are located. The characteristics of the synapses must also be known. With the multiplicity of connections and the different types of synapses, even a small fragment of the central nervous system is extraordinarily complicated. It is a great tribute to the students of the spinal cord that the analysis of reflex behavior in terms of nerve cells has progressed so far.

A misleading byproduct of reflex analysis is the idea that the nervous system sits quietly, waiting for a stimulus to arrive. Nothing could be further from the truth. To begin with, most sense organs continually send impulses into the central nervous system. In the intact animal there are excitatory and inhibitory pathways from the brain which are always modulating the activity of cells in the spinal cord. When an animal is absolutely still, the nervous system is not silent; the excitatory and inhibitory inputs on the motoneurons are precisely balanced.

SYSTEMS ANALYSIS Even when the properties of individual alpha- and gamma-motoneurons, stretch receptors, and muscle fibers are understood, it is difficult to anticipate how hundreds or thousands of them work together to produce a smoothly graded movement. And, of course, the more complicated the movement, the more difficult it is to piece together from the components of the reflex chain.

Some investigators have tried to bypass these difficulties by adopting the method devised by control systems engineers for analyzing manmade information processing systems. The components are treated as a collection of linked black boxes, thus the system can be analyzed without knowledge of how they actually operate. The transmission pathways between the boxes must be worked out, then the system can be summarized as a functional diagram (Figure 2-20). Experiments are devised to determine how the output of each box varies with a change in input. This is the "transfer function" of the component. The transfer function may be shown as a graph relating output to input, or as a mathematical equation. Once this is done, the entire system can be put

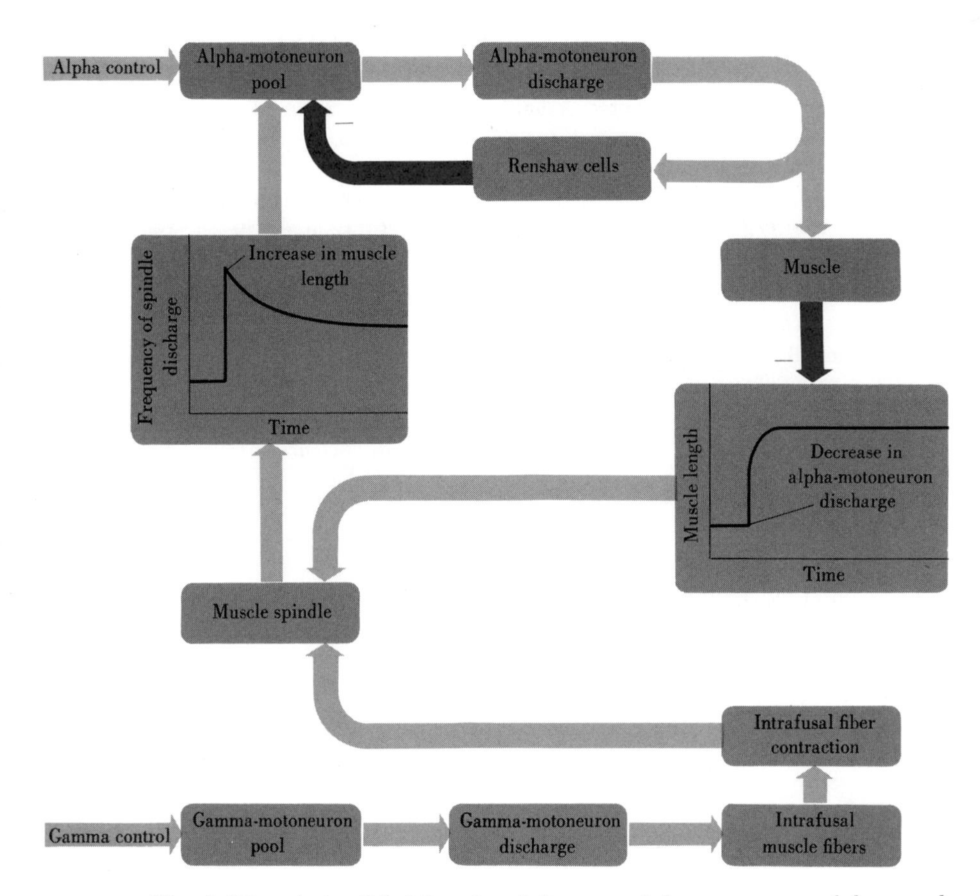

Fig. 2-20 *A simplified functional diagram of the components of the stretch reflex. The inserts show the "transfer functions" between alpha-motoneuron discharge and muscle length and between muscle length and the frequency of stretch receptor discharge. If all of the transfer functions at each step reflex were obtained, a complete quantitative description of the behavior would be possible.*

together as a mathematical model, or it can be reconstructed on an analog computer.

The systems approach has been used in the analysis of certain spinal reflexes and also for studies of more complicated behavior, such as the tracking and capture of flies by the praying mantis. In some cases the analysis has lead to predictions about the behavior of the animal which were then tested and found to be true. This approach may be a tremendous help in putting together information about complex behavioral systems.

FURTHER READING

Baker, P. F., "The Nerve Axon," *Scientific American* (March 1966), p. 74.

Brazier, M. A. B., *Electrical Activity of the Nervous System.* New York: Macmillan, 1961.

Eccles, Sir J. C., "The Synapse," *Scientific American* (January 1965), p. 56.

——, *The Physiology of Synapses.* New York: Academic Press, 1964.

Galambos, R., *Nerves and Muscles.* Garden City, N. Y.: Doubleday, 1962.

Griffin, D. R., *Animal Structure and Function*, Modern Biology Series. New York: Holt, Rinehart and Winston, 1962.

Katz, B., "How Cells Communicate," *Scientific American* (September 1961), p. 209.

——, *Nerve, Muscle, and Synapse.* New York: McGraw-Hill, 1966.

Keynes, R., "The Nerve Impulse and the Squid," *Scientific American* (December 1958), p. 83.

Ochs, S., *Elements of Neurophysiology.* New York: Wiley, 1965.

Sherrington, C. S., *Integrative Action of the Nervous System*, 2d ed. New Haven, Conn.: Yale University Press, 1947.

Wilson, V. J., "Inhibition in the Central Nervous System," *Scientific American* (May 1966), p. 102.

chapter 3

Reflexes and the Behavior of Coelenterates

The success achieved on spinal animals naturally led to the idea that the behavior of simple animals might be completely understood by studying their reflexes. This was the starting point for behavioral studies on the coelenterates, which indicate both the effectiveness and the limitations of reflex analysis.

The coelenterates are animals with an extreme diversity of body form and of habit, ranging from sessile anemones and hydroids to the free-swimming medusa (Figure 3-1). Since the behavior of the sessile forms is simpler, we will begin our study with them. The anemone does not have a central nervous system; there is no large aggregation of nerve cell bodies, axons and dendrites. Instead the nerve cells and their processes

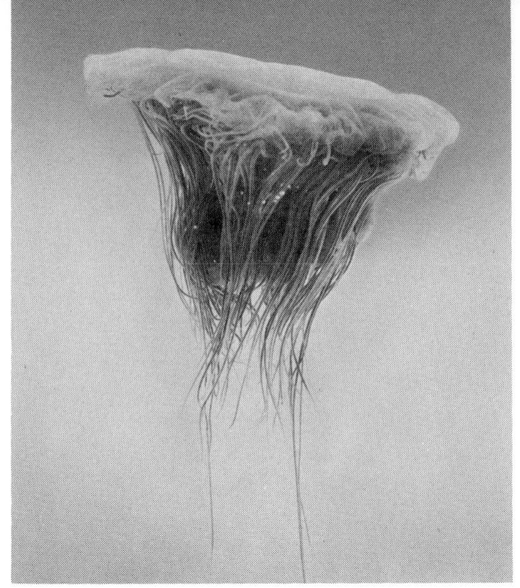

Fig. 3-1 *(A) An anemone from the coast of Florida. It holds to the rock with its pedal disc. At the top of its column are the many tentacles. The mouth, which cannot be seen in this photograph, is surrounded by the tentacles. (B) A medusa from the sea off Nova Scotia. It swims by rhythmically contracting the bell. Prey is caught by the tentacles extending below the animal and is carried up to the mouth in the center of the bell. (Both by R. C. Hermes, National Audubon Society.)*

are distributed as a meshwork throughout the tissues as a nerve net. The nerve cells, here as in other animals, have the property of selectively taking up the dye, methylene blue, so the structure of the nerve net can then be traced by using the light microscope (Figure 3-2). For many years there was uncertainty and argument about the anatomy of the junctions between the nerve cells. It now seems that in most cases there is some sort of synapse and not a direct continuity between the nerve cells when they meet, as was once believed.

Fig. 3-2 *The arrangement of nerve cells in the nerve net of the sea anemone. (After Batham, Pantin, and Robson,* Quarterly Journal of Microscopical Science*).*

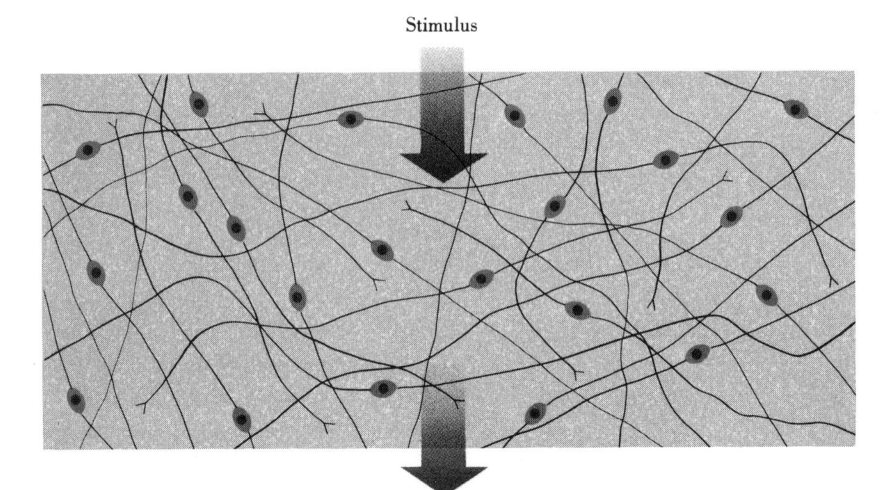

THE WITHDRAWAL RESPONSE

To the casual observer, an anemone in an aquarium seems passive, reacting only when there is an obvious external stimulus.

One way to get the anemone to do something is to prod it with a glass rod. The body will be withdrawn from the stimulus. If the prod is sufficiently intense, the tentacles will be pulled in and the anemone will round itself into a compact ball. Retraction can also be elicited by using an electrical shock as the stimulus. A single shock is seldom effective; a short train of stimuli are needed to produce the response. This simple form of temporal summation is called facilitation. A single brief touch evokes a response because the sensory receptors fire a burst of impulses following the briefest stimulus.

Similar responses can be produced in a strip cut from the body wall of an anemone. When a train of stimuli is given at one point on the strip, a wave of contraction spreads over the tissue. If any point on the strip is stimulated, the response will begin to spread from this point, moving in all directions over the strip. The diffuse nature of the conducting path is shown by experiments in which one end of a strip is stimulated and the response is recorded at the other end. At a number of points along the length of the strip, cuts are made from one edge almost to the other edge (Figure 3-3). As long as there is a bridge of intact tissue stretching from one end of the strip to the other, excitation is conducted over the entire strip. For many years it was thought that the behavior of the strip reflects the diffuse nature of the nerve net.

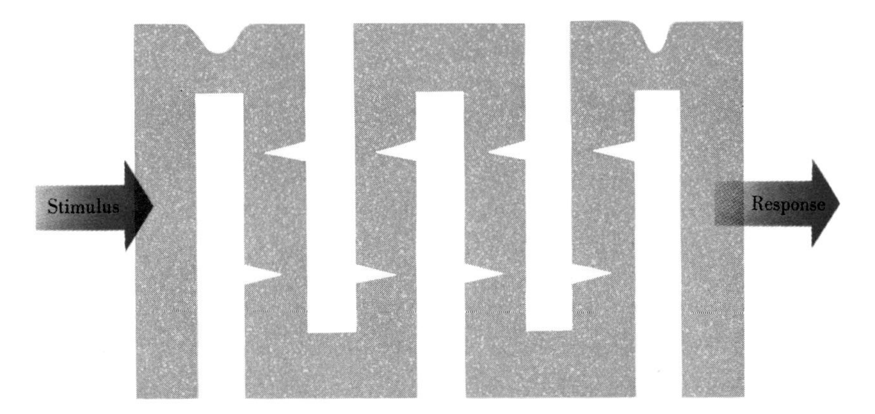

Fig. 3-3 *The preparation used to demonstrate the diffuse pathway for conduction in coelenterates. A medusa was cut so that direct pathways would be eliminated. Nevertheless, a stimulus on one side still produces a response on the further side. (Redrawn from* Structure and Function in the Nervous Systems of Invertebrates *by Theodore Holmes Bulloch and G. Adrian Horridge. W. H. Freeman and Company. Copyright © 1965).*

The bridge of tissue remaining after the cut almost certainly contains a nerve fiber. And excitation set up at one point was thought to spread in all directions throughout the nerve net. If this idea is correct, then the synapses in the nerve net either conduct in both directions, unlike almost all other synapses in the animal kingdom, or adjacent neurons might be connected by two synapses, the first conducting in one direction and the second conducting in the reverse direction. Recently it has been shown that in some coelenterates excitation can be conducted from one epithelial cell to another. In these simple animals, ordinary epithelial cells, as well as neurons, are excitable. Perhaps the diffuse conduction through a strip of body wall goes by way of the epithelial cells and not in the nerve net.

The faster responses shown by coelenterates undoubtedly are conducted through a nerve net. For example, the umbrella part of the medusa normally contracts as a unit to propel the swimming animal. The central part of the umbrella can be cut away, leaving a doughnut-shaped ring of tissue. If a point on the ring is stimulated, waves of contraction start going around each side of the ring. The contraction waves meet on the opposite side and stop; in the regions where the waves have just passed all of the neurons are refractory. Occasionally one of the two waves fails to propagate from the point of stimulation. The contraction wave starts around one side of the ring and returns around the other side. When the contraction wave reaches the point first stimulated, the neurons in this region are no longer refractory, and the wave goes around again, and again, and again. In one famous instance, the wave continued going around a ring for eleven days, traveling at a speed of 77.5 centimeters per second. The contraction wave traveled about 457 miles before it stopped.

FACILITATION In spite of the diffuse connections in the nerve net, the distance excitation travels and the magnitude of the response given by a coelenterate often depends on the intensity of the initial stimulus. A light touch may produce only a localized movement; as the stimulus intensity is increased, more and more of the animal responds. The response is graded because single impulses are not transmitted across the junctions in the nerve nets. An impulse is set up on the far side of the junction only after two, three, or even more impulses arrive at the ending of the prejunctional cell. This process is called facilitation. This means that at each junction more impulses arrive on the near side than leave on the far side. Excitation diminishes as it spreads from the point of stimulation through the nerve net (Figure 3-4).

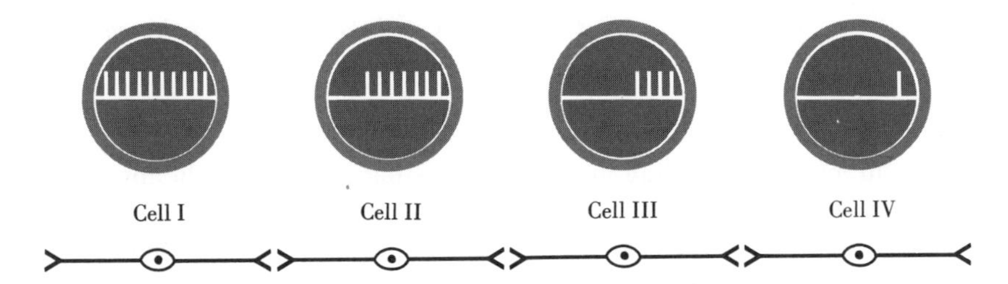

Fig. 3-4 *In the nerve net facilitation is often necessary for junctional transmission. Several impulses must reach the prejunctional terminal before an impulse is set up in the next cell in the net. Therefore, excitation diminishes as it spreads away from the stimulated point.*

FEEDING BEHAVIOR Coelenterates are armed with different types of nematocysts. The nematocysts are cells that discharge a filament when stimulated. Some types of nematocysts have pointed filaments with barbs beneath the tip which can pierce an animal (Figure 3-5). The nematocysts are discharged by mechanical stimuli produced by contact with another object. This is the first step in the capture of prey. Once a hydra has discharged the first nematocysts, it begins to wave about its tentacles and to move its mouth, or oral disc. If fresh hydra are now gently transferred into the same solution, they also begin feeding movements. This experiment suggests that when the nematocysts are discharged, a chemical is

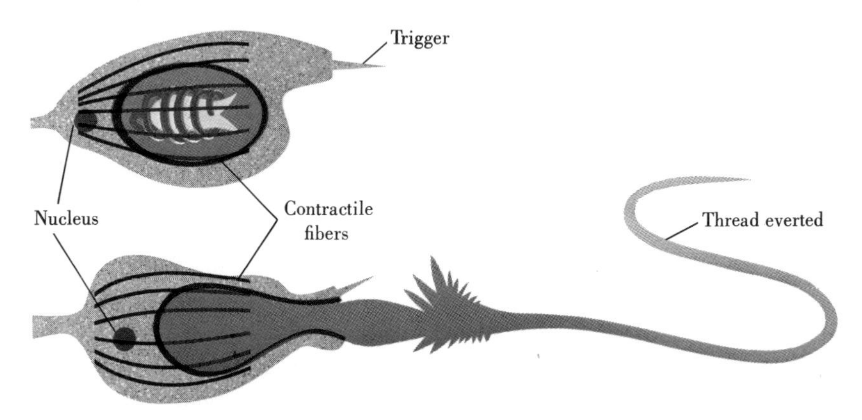

Fig. 3-5 *One type of nematocyst from a coelenterate. When something brushes against the trigger, the thread is rapidly shot out. The barbs will penetrate the skin or cuticle of a prey and the thread will enter. Many nematocysts make stinging or paralyzing chemicals that are injected through the thread. (By permission of the University of Chicago Press. From* Animals without Backbones *by Ralph Buchsbaum.)*

released into the external solution; this substance acts on the animal to promote feeding behavior. The nature of the chemical trigger is unknown.

If a nematocyst is shot out so that it pierces another animal, then tissue fluids begin to leak from the prey into the water. These fluids, or meat juices added to the water by an experimenter, lower the threshold for the discharge of other nematocysts.

ANEMONES, WHELKS, AND HERMIT CRABS

The behavior shown by some anemones, controlled only by nerve nets, is almost incredibly complex. There is an anemone from European waters that often lives on the shell of one species of whelk (a large marine snail). A hermit crab may occupy the shell when it no longer contains the whelk.

An anemone which is living without a shell will almost always attach itself, if offered a shell of the proper species of whelk. Occasionally the anemone will even attach itself to shells of other species. Since shells lose all attraction to the anemone if they are boiled in acid or alkali, it is apparent that they contain an attractive chemical.

There are four steps in the transfer of an anemone to the whelk shell:

1. Some of the anemone's tentacles brush against the shell. The stalk of the anemone then extends, and the unattached tentacles wave at a faster rate. As each tentacle blunders into the shell, it is attached. Soon the entire ring of tentacles is adhering to the shell and the oral disc is also attached. The anemone is now bent in the shape of an inverted U, fastened by its tentacles to the shell and by its pedal disc to its old attachment.

2. The pedal disc is freed from the old attachment. The first sign of disengagement is the flow of peristaltic waves down the column of the anemone, starting near the oral disc and running toward the foot. The column begins to thin and to elongate. This frees the pedal disc from the mucous envelope which formed the old attachment.

3. Now the anemone must move the pedal disc onto the shell. The column bends, bringing the pedal disc toward the shell. At the same time the pedal disc begins to swell, until it looks like a grotesque mushroom. The tenacles start to shift their hold on the shell, moving over toward one edge, so there is space on the shell for placing the pedal disc.

4. The next ten to fifteen minutes are used for attaching the pedal disc to the shell. Then the tentacles and oral disc loosen their hold on the shell and the anemone resumes a normal posture.

The behavior is even more extraordinary when the whelk shell is inhabited by a hermit crab. Some crabs take no part in the transfer of an anemone to the shell. Other crabs, from the same species and from the same population, take an active role in the transfer. Scientists have not yet been able to determine why some crabs help and others do not.

The participating crabs begin by prodding and striking the anemone, which causes the anemone to loosen the attachment of its pedal disc. Once the anemone is free, the crab lifts it toward the shell. If the anemone does not fasten to the shell with its tentacles at this step, the crab drops the anemone and stops all efforts to make the transfer. If the anemone does fasten on with its tentacles, the crab holds the foot of the anemone on the shell until the pedal disc makes a new attachment.

This behavior seems remarkably complex to be coordinated by a nerve net. It shows how substantial a behavioral capacity can be built into an anatomically simple network. But another view can also be taken. Many coelenterates have about 100,000 neurons in the nerve net. There are about the same number of nerve cells in the central nervous system of a honeybee. The behavior of the honeybee is almost incomparably more complicated. A great deal more can be done with the same number of nerve cells when they are put together in an optimal way.

PACEMAKERS When the experimental analysis is complete, the behavior by which the anemone transfers itself to the shell will probably be described as a chain of reflexes, in which each response puts the animal in a situation where it receives the stimulus for the next act. However, there are some clear examples of coelenterate behavior that cannot be described as a response to stimuli originating in the external world. Some behavior is generated within the animal. For example, medusae swim by rhythmically contracting their umbrellas. Each contraction is initiated by nerve impulses that arise spontaneously. The spontaneous impulses are generated in any one of eight clusters of nerve cells, or pacemakers, which are evenly spaced around the circumference of the umbrella. The clusters are the marginal bodies. The impulse started at one of the marginal bodies sweeps across the umbrella, causing the muscles to contract. When the impulse reaches the other marginal bodies, it resets them back to their initial condition. Each of the marginal bodies then starts again on the process leading toward the generation of an impulse. The first one to fire sets off another beat of the umbrella and also resets the other pacemakers. Medusae continue to swim as long as they have one marginal body to set the pace; the other seven can be removed without stopping the beat.

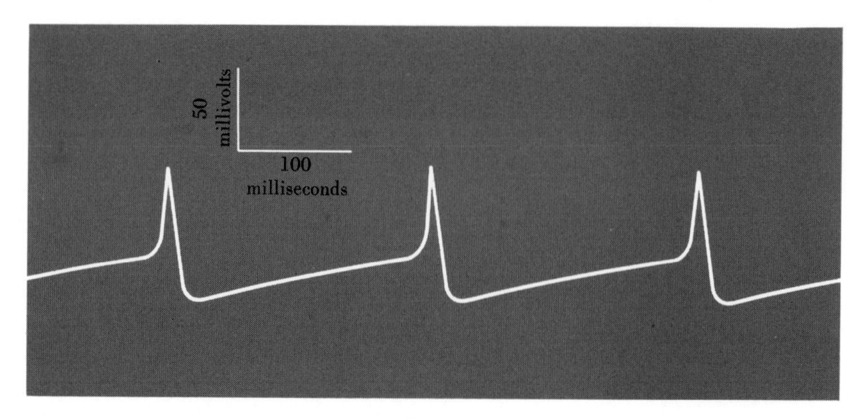

Fig. 3-6 *Spontaneous nerve impulses generated in the neuron in the central nervous system of a mollusk. As soon as the spike is over, the potential gradually starts to fall until threshold is reached and a new spike is set up. (An experiment by L. Tauc. From* Structure and Function in the Nervous System of Invertebrates *by Theodore Holmes Bulloch and G. Adrian Horridge. W. H. Freeman and Company. Copyright © 1965.)*

The mechanism by which spontaneous impulses are generated in the neurons of the marginal bodies is unknown. However, intracellular electrical recordings have been made from a number of types of nerve cells in different animals which are generating spontaneous nerve impulses. These cells do not have a stable resting potential; instead, the potential across the membrane starts to drift down until threshold is reached and the cell generates an action potential (Figure 3-6). The membrane then repolarizes, but the potential immediately starts to drift down once again. Presumably, there are similar sorts of cells on the marginal bodies.

The swimming beat is the most obvious example in the behavior of coelenterates of the role played by the spontaneous generation of nerve impulses, yet it is not the only one. If an anemone is tied to a light lever which traces on a slowly moving drum, the pattern of the tracing shows that even in a constant environment, there are slow, rhythmic movements. The movements are far too slow to be seen by the naked eye. In the intact animal, a special region of the nerve net is responsible for generating the slow movements. However, isolated strips of body wall are also often spontaneously active, so, under the proper circumstances, many of the cells of the nerve net can fire spontaneously. The spontaneous activity pattern of anemones is drastically changed if a dilute extract of clam is added to the water. The animal then elongates and extends its tentacles. When the water is changed, the animal retracts and the rhythmic movements are taken up once again.

The closer one looks, the more facets there are to the behavior of the coelenterates. Even with their simple anatomy, there are many gaps and uncertainties in our knowledge of the physiological basis of their behavior. The complexity is scarcely unexpected. Even for sessile animals the demands of the environment are far from simple. All living species must sucessfully cope with their normal environments or they are on the verge of extinction. Each has met the evolutionary test of time and has evolved behavior appropriate to its way of life.

FURTHER READING

Batham, E. J., C. F. A. Pantin, and E. A. Robson, "The Nerve Net of the Sea Anemone, *Metridium senile* (L): The Mesenteries and Column," *Quarterly Journal of Microscopical Science*, vol. 101 (1960), p. 487.

Crowell, Sears, ed., "Behavior Physiology of Coelenterates," *American Zoologist*, vol. 5 (1965), p. 335.

Pantin, C. F. A., "Behavior Patterns in Lower Invertebrates," *Symposia Society Experimental Biology*, vol. 4 (1950), p. 175.

Prosser, C. L., and F. A. Brown, *Comparative Animal Physiology*, Philadelphia: Saunders, 1961.

Ross, D. M., and L. Sutton, "The Response of the Sea Anemone *Calliactis parasitica* to Shells of the Hermit Crab *Pagurus bernhardus*," *Proceedings of the Royal Society*, vol. 155B (1961), p. 266.

chapter **4**

Three Sense Organs

A reflex is started by the excitation of a sense organ. Everything we know about the world around us, or about the inner world within our bodies, comes through the windows provided by the sense organs. To understand the behavior of an animal, we must know what stimuli its sense organs can detect. Sense organs take in physical energy and give out a series of nerve impulses. Because they transduce some form of physical energy into a nervous signal, sense organs are often called transducers.

THE CRUSTACEAN STRETCH RECEPTOR Reflex systems are understood largely from the studies on the spinal cord of the cat. Our understanding of sensory receptors was greatly advanced by

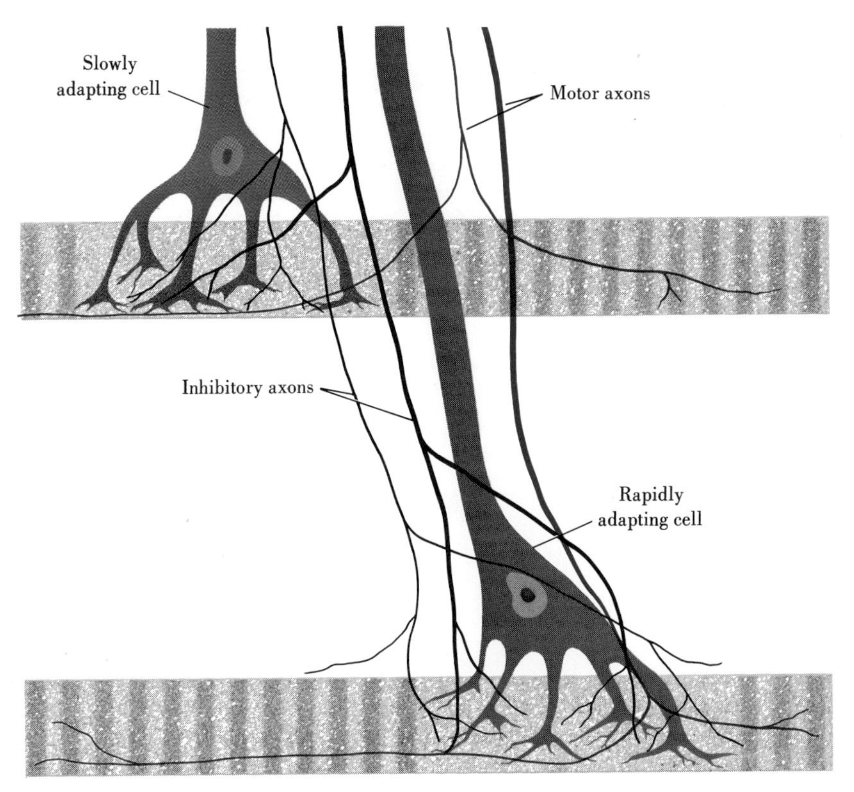

Fig. 4-1 *The two stretch receptors from one side of an abdominal segment of the crayfish. The axons from the receptors run to the central nervous system. Coming from the central nervous system are inhibitory axons and motor axons that cause contraction of the muscle on which the receptors are sitting. (From* Structure and Function in the Nervous System of Invertebrates *by Theodore Holmes Bulloch and G. Adrian Horridge. W. H. Freeman and Company. Copyright © 1965.)*

experiments on the abdominal stretch receptors of crayfish and lobsters because they show all of the fundamental features of sense organs in a form ready for experimental investigations.

In every abdominal segment of a crayfish, there are four stretch receptors, two on either side of the body. Each stretch receptor has a single muscle fiber that runs from the exoskeleton of one segment across the joint to the exoskeleton of the next segment. If the joint between the two segments is extended, the muscle fiber is stretched. The central portion of the muscle fiber lacks striations and is not contractile. Mounted on the central portion of the stretch receptor is the cell body of a sensory neuron. The axon runs from the cell body into the central nervous system (Figure 4-1). The dendrites of the sensory neuron form a meshwork over the central portion of the muscle fiber. When the muscle fiber is stretched, the dendrites are pulled out.

A microelectrode can be inserted into the cell body. As expected, the inside of the cell is about −70 millivolts compared to the outside solution. Figure 4-2 shows what happens when the sense organ is stretched. At first, only a slight stretch is applied. The potential across

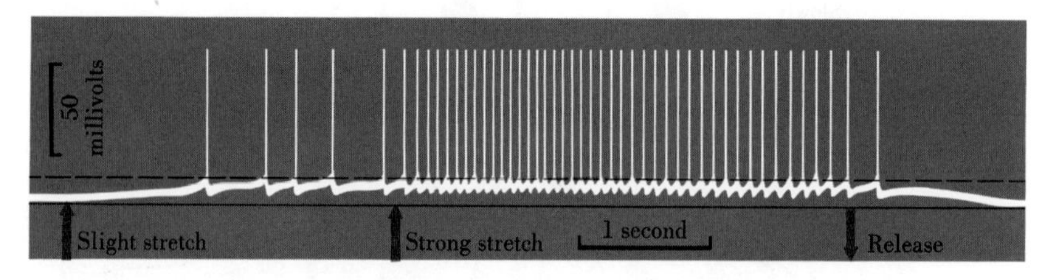

Fig. 4-2 *A record made with an intracellular microelectrode inserted into a crayfish stretch receptor. The dashed line indicates the threshold for setting up an action potential. (Adapted from Eyzaguirre and Kuffler. Reprinted by permission of the Rockefeller University Press from the* Journal of General Physiology, *vol. 39, September 1955, p. 101.)*

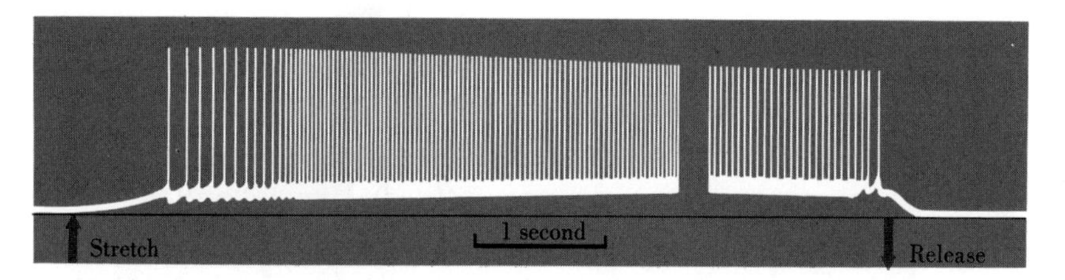

Fig. 4-3 *A record made with an intracellular electrode in a stretch receptor. During the first part of the experiment the stretch was gradually increased, resulting in a larger generator potential and an increased firing rate. The gap in the record is of a period of several seconds during which the recording is not reproduced. After the interval the firing rate is still high; this is the slowly adapting receptor. (Adapted from Eyzaguirre and Kuffler. Reprinted by permission of the Rockefeller University Press from the* Journal of General Physiology, *vol. 39, September 1955, p. 158.)*

the membrane begins to decrease. The cell continues to depolarize until threshold is reached and an action potential is generated. As soon as the action potential is over, the cell begins to depolarize again. The rate of depolarization depends on the extent of the stretch, so the frequency of impulse generation also depends on stretch.

A detailed experimental analysis shows that the depolarization takes place in the dendrites. The depolarization spreads to the cell body because an electrical current flows between two portions of the cell when their membranes are at different potentials. The depolarization is called the generator potential. When the generator potential reaches threshold, an action potential is set up. The action potential is conducted over the cell body and down the axon, but it does not invade the dendrites. They remain depolarized. As soon as the action potential in the cell body is over, the current between the dendrites and the cell body begins to flow again, the cell body is depolarized, and another action potential is generated.

The size of the generator potential depends on the stretch given to the dendrites. And the rate of firing in the sensory nerve is proportional to the size of the generator potential. These relations are graphically illustrated in Figure 4-3. At the moment indicated by the arrow, the receptor was stretched and for the next four seconds the stretch was steadily increased. Both the size of the generator potential and the rate of nerve discharge increased steadily. There was a gap in the record, during which the receptor was held at a constant length for several seconds. After this interval, the generator potential was slightly smaller and the frequency of the action potentials had decreased; the receptor had adapted somewhat to the steady stimulus. At the second arrow the stretch was released, the generator potential fell off, and firing ceased.

Adaptation occurs slowly in the stretch receptor whose behavior was just described. The second stretch receptor on the same side, in each segment of the body, adapts rapidly. Given a constant stretch, the generator potential and the rate of firing quickly decline. In the animal, the slowly adapting receptor reports on the stretch on the segment at any time. The rapidly adapting receptor is thrown into a burst of activity when the animal moves to a new position.

The muscle fiber which forms part of the stretch receptor is innervated by a motor nerve from the central nervous system. Contraction of the muscle pulls out the central region of the fiber and stretches the dendrites on the receptor cell. The crayfish has a system quite like the gamma-motoneuron system of the vertebrates.

The crayfish can control the input from the stretch receptor in another way as well. An axon, running from the central nervous system out to the sensory neuron, branches repeatedly and synapses at many points on the dendrites. The efferent axon is called the I-fiber. Suppose that the stretch receptor is pulled out, so the sensory neuron is firing a steady series of action potentials. The I-axon is then stimulated to conduct a burst of impulses out to the receptor. The firing of the stretch receptor stops completely (Figure 4-4). The I-axon is inhibitory. It acts

Fig. 4-4 *A recording from a stretch receptor showing the effects produced by stimulating the inhibitory nerve. (Adapted from Eyzaguirre and Kuffler. Reprinted by permission at the Rockefeller University Press from the* Journal of General Physiology, *vol. 39, September 1955, p. 158.)*

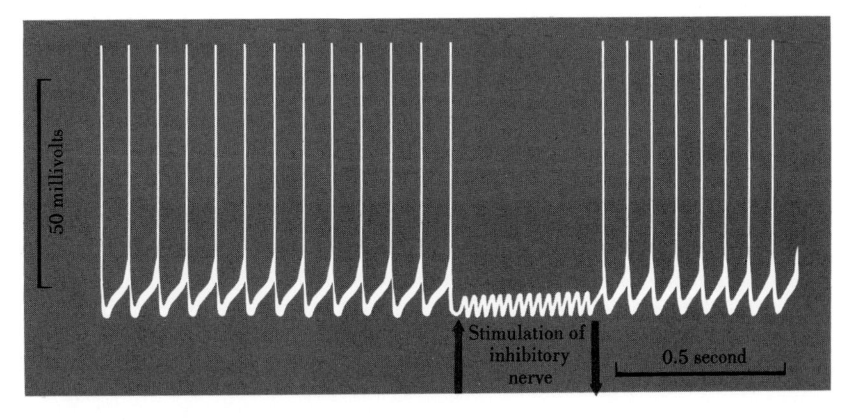

on the dendrites in the same way that inhibitory synapses work on spinal motoneurons.

There are many other examples of inhibitory neurons running from the central nervous system to sense organs, or at least to synapses early in the sensory pathway. Indeed, this arrangement is probably the rule rather than the exception. The central nervous system can use inhibition to regulate sensory inflow; reports from certain sense organs can be minimized in favor of messages of greater importance to the animal. This is undoubtedly part of the mechanism for choosing from the wide variety of incoming messages and selecting a single motor outflow.

THE MAMMALIAN EAR

Many animals have sense organs built on the same general plan as the crustacean stretch receptor: mechanical energy is focused so that it pulls or pushes on a nerve ending and thus sets up impulses. This principle is used in our own stretch receptors, in mechanoreceptors in the skin, in the muscle tendons, at specialized points on blood vessels, and so forth. But further elaboration is required to make the most sensitive kind of mechanoreceptor. Our ear responds to the mechanical energy of traveling waves in the air. If the ear became only slightly more sensitive, all we could hear would be a roar generated by the random movements of molecules. In other words, the ear is a sense organ which has evolved almost to the conceivable limits of sensitivity.

The first problem in hearing is to transfer the energy of movements of the air to the movement of a fluid, since the sensory receptors lie in a fluid-filled chamber. The transfer of sound from air to water is extremely inefficient, as is well known to anyone who has ducked his head under water when someone is talking at the edge of the pool. Most of the sound is reflected back from the surface of the water. The problem is solved by having the sound waves in the air first move a membrane stretched like a drum. The eardrum, or tympanic membrane, is easily moved by sound. The movements of the eardrum are transmitted by three tiny levers of bone, the auditory ossicles, to move another membrane, the oval window (Figure 4-5). The oval window is at the interface between air and water. The movements of the oval window set up waves in the fluid of the cochlea. The fluid in the cochlea can move because there is another membrane, the round window, which can be pushed back and forth by waves in the cochlea.

The cochlea is subdivided by membranes into three sections (Figure 4-6). The movement of the fluid in the cochlea causes the flexible basilar membrane to move up and down. As the basilar membrane

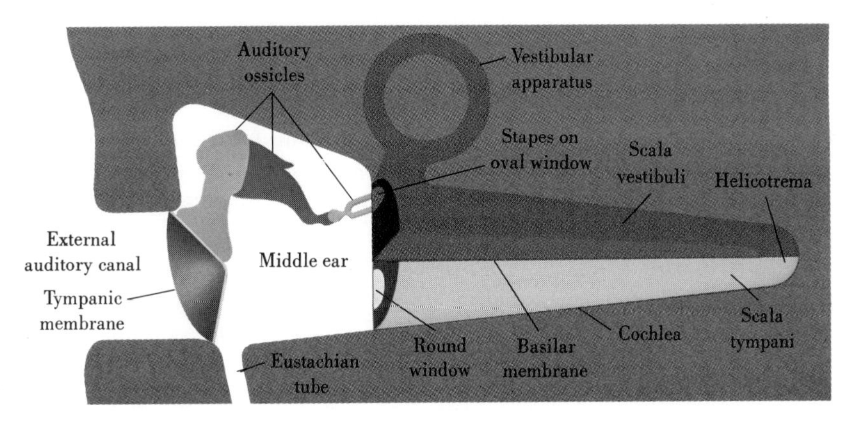

Fig. 4-5 *The anatomy of the human ear. The coiled cochlea has been unrolled in the diagram to show how the basilar membrane subdivides the inner ear into fluid-filled compartments. Fluid can move from the scala vestibuli to the scala tympani by way of the helicotrema. (After Békésy and Rosenblith, "The Mechanical Properties of the Ear," in* Handbook of Experimental Psychology. *S. S. Stevens, ed.)*

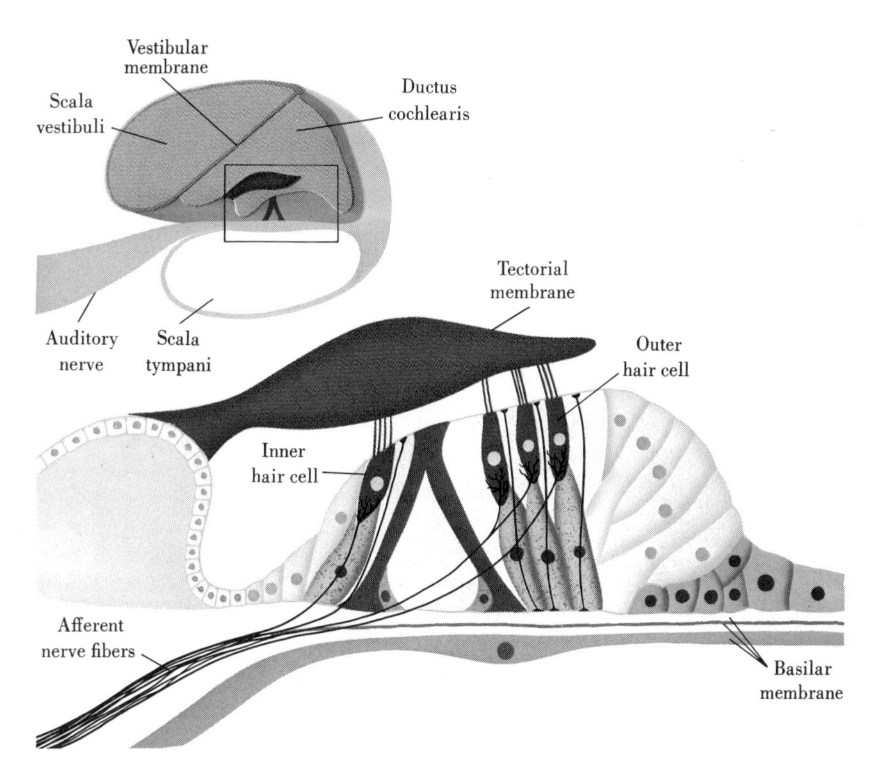

Fig. 4-6 *A cross section of the cochlea showing the relation of the afferent fibers to the hair cells and the attachment of the hairs to the tectorial membrane. (After H. Davis,* Handbook of Physiology, *vol. 1, American Physiological Society.)*

moves, the hairs on the hair cells are bent back and forth because they are attached to the tectorial membrane which is relatively immobile. The movement of the hairs leads, in a somewhat indirect way, to action potentials in the auditory nerve.

The fluid in the ductus cochlearis is maintained at a potential of about 80 millivolts positive to the fluid in the scala vestibuli and in the scala tympani. (The mechanism generating the potential is unknown, but there is always a potential across the hair cells in the basilar membrane.) When the hairs are bent, there is a change in the electrical resistance of the hair cells. Therefore, an electrical current flows through the basilar membrane. The current flowing through the basilar membrane may produce the generator potential that excites the inner ear. The nerve endings are at the base of the hair cells (Figure 4-7). It is unclear whether the nerve endings are excited directly by the current flowing through the basilar membrane, or the hair cells are excited first and then transmit to the neurons, perhaps by releasing a transmitter.

The current flowing through the basilar membrane produces a changing voltage which can be recorded between an electrode on the round window (see Figure 4-5) and an electrode at some distant point on the body. This potential is called the cochlear microphonic. The basilar membrane vibrates at the same frequency as the sound stimulus. Therefore, the cochlear microphonic also has the same frequency. Since the cochlear microphonic can be recorded rather easily, it is often used to evaluate cochlear function in cases of human deafness or to estimate the sensitivity and range of the ears of other mammals.

Fig. 4-7 *The relation between the afferent endings of the nerve fibers from the auditory nerve and the hair cells, as shown by the electron microscope. (After H. Enström and J. Wersäll,* Experimental Cell Research Supp. 5, *Academic Press Inc.)*

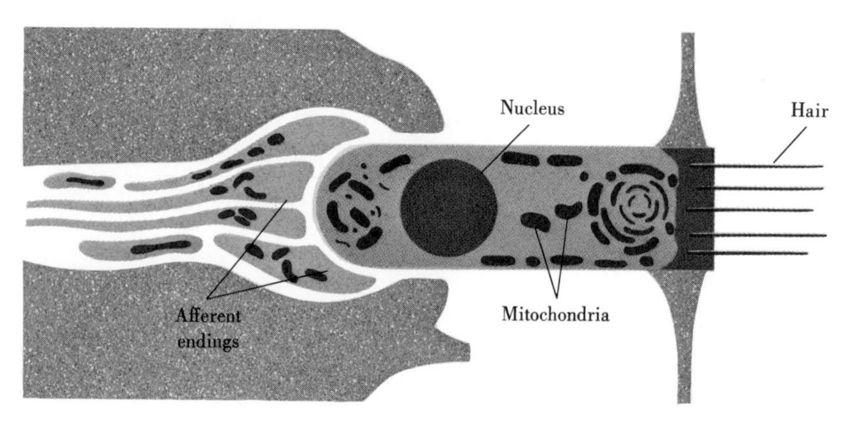

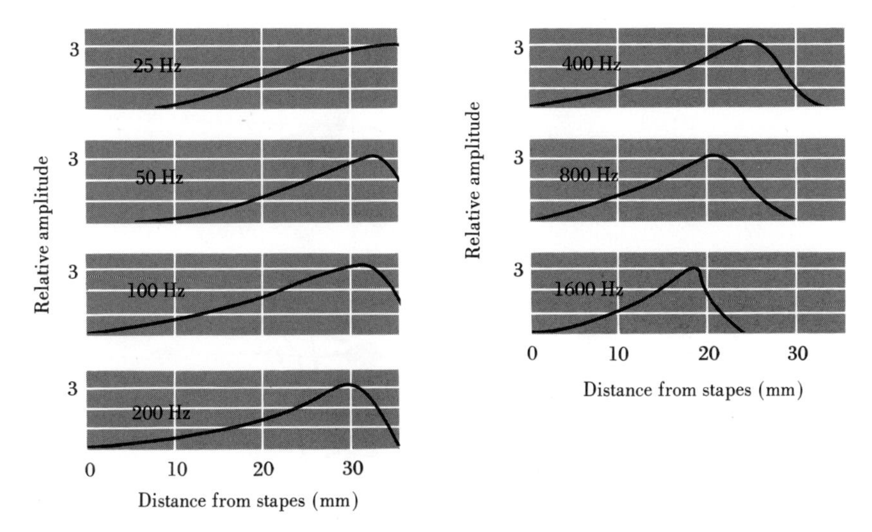

Fig. 4-8 *A diagram of the movements of different parts of the basilar membrane in response to sound of different frequencies. Low frequency sounds move the basilar membrane at the end of the cochlea near the helicotrema. High frequency sounds move the end near the oval and round windows. (Adapted from Békésy and Rosenblith, "The Mechanical Properties of the Ear," in* Handbook of Experimental Psychology, *S. S. Stevens, ed.)*

How is the frequency of the sound communicated to the central nervous system? A young human can hear sounds above 16,000 Hertz (Hz; cycles per second). If the stimulus is a sound wave with a frequency below 1000 Hz, the fibers in the auditory nerve fire in synchrony with the movements of the basilar membrane. The frequency of the stimulus is probably coded directly as the frequency of firing in the auditory nerve. The direct code could not possibly work with higher frequency sounds because the auditory nerve fibers cannot conduct more than 1000 spikes per second. The sound waves set up a standing wave on the basilar membrane, so one point on the membrane is displaced the furthest (Figure 4-8). The neurons which come from this furthest point fire at the highest frequency. Higher frequency stimuli are coded by the place on the basilar membrane where nerve impulses are set up at the fastest rate.

The movements of the basilar membrane are never sharply localized. With any sound frequency large portions of the basilar membrane will move and many nerve fibers will be excited. Nevertheless, normal individuals can distinguish between 256 Hz (middle C) and 259 Hz. There must be some accurate mechanism telling the central nervous system which part of the basilar membrane is vibrating with the greatest amplitude. The mechanism will be described along with the pathway conducting auditory impulses into the central nervous system (see Chapter 5, Auditory Pathways).

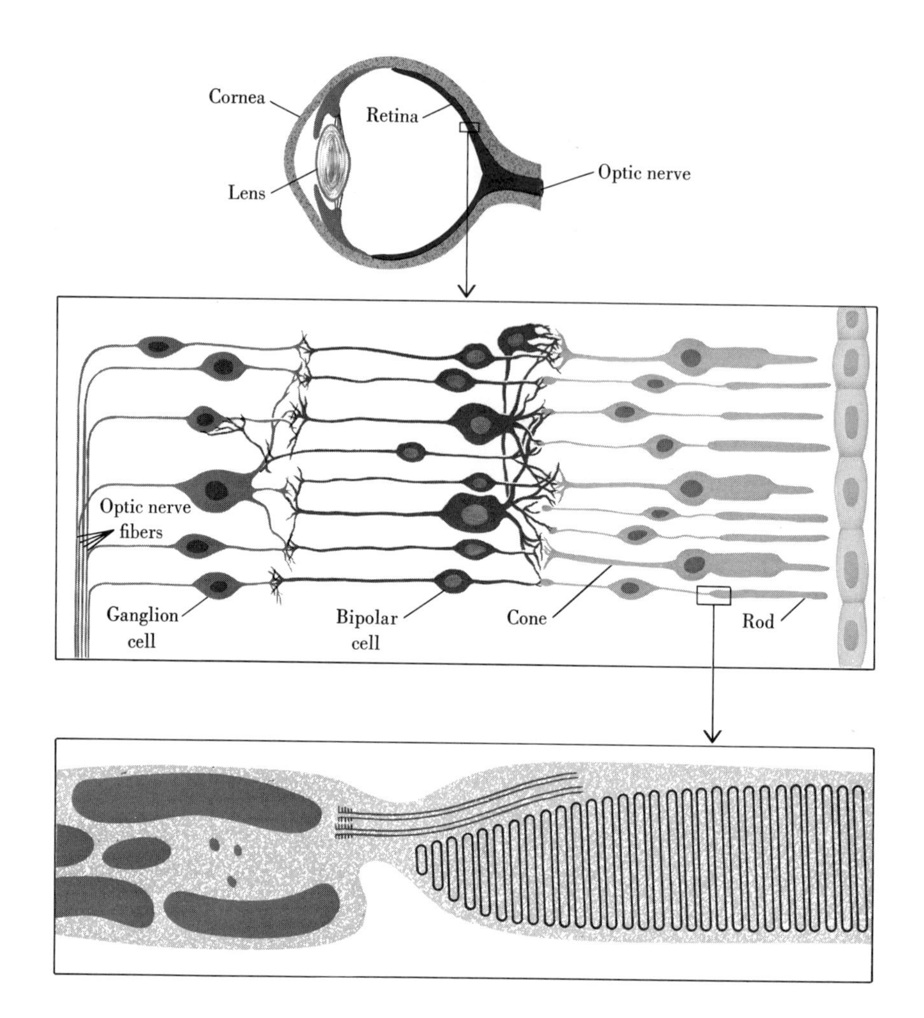

Fig. 4-9 *Three views of the visual receptor in man. A cross section of the entire eye* (upper). *A view of a part of the retina* (middle). *Notice that the receptors, the rods and cones, are at the rear of the retina. Light must pass through the layers containing nerve cells before it reaches the receptors. Many receptors may converge on one bipolar cell and many bipolar cells may converge on one ganglion cell. There are also other types of cells that make lateral connections within the retina. An electron microscopic view of part of a rod* (bottom). *The visual pigment is arranged in the stacked membranes. In the stalk connecting the two sections of the rod is a cilium, which may be important in transmitting excitation from the outer segment toward the cell body of the rod. (Adapted from W. Telfer and D. Kennedy,* The Biology of Organisms, *1965.)*

VISION There are still many gaps in our understanding of how light energy is transduced into nerve impulses. In the mammalian eye, the incoming light is focused by the lens onto the retina, in the same way that a camera lens focuses an image on the film (Figure 4-9). There are two types of primary sense cells in the retina, the rods and the cones.

The rods have an outer segment containing a stack of leaflike layers. The layers contain the visual pigment, rhodopsin (visual purple). Rhodopsin is made of a carotinoid pigment, retinal, conjugated to a protein, opsin. When a photon of light is absorbed by a molecule of rhodopsin, the pigment undergoes a series of steric and chemical changes. The rhodopsin splits into protein and carotinoid and loses its red color. It has been bleached by the light. Rhodopsin is then resynthesized. In some unknown way, the bleaching of a single rhodopsin molecule is sufficient to excite the rod. When two to fourteen rods are excited at the same instant, an observer reports seeing a faint flash of light. The rod is excited only if the light is absorbed by rhodopsin. Therefore, there should be a close relation between the ability of rhodopsin to absorb light of different wave lengths and the sensitivity of the eye. This is indeed the case (Figure 4-10).

When an animal is in daylight or in an illuminated room, a large fraction of the rhodopsin in the eye is bleached at any given moment. The rhodopsin concentration is kept up only because the rate of resynthesis matches the rate of breakdown. In a dark room resynthesis goes on, but there is little bleaching, so the rhodopsin concentration in the retina goes up markedly. As the rhodopsin concentration rises,

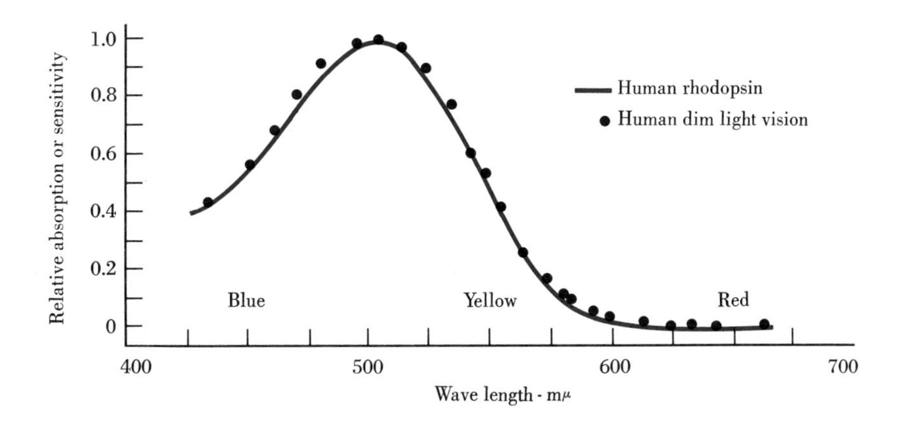

Fig. 4-10 *The absorption of a rhodopsin solution compared to the sensitivity of a man to dim light at different wave lengths. (G. Wald and P. Brown, "Human Rhodopsin,"* Science, *vol. 127, 31 January 1958, pp. 222–226.)*

the eye becomes more sensitive. The threshold for seeing dim flashes of light is lowered. The eye becomes dark adapted. Rhodopsin is not bleached by red light (Figure 4-10), so dark adaptation can also go on in red light or if one wears red goggles. These methods for dark adapting are used by night fighter pilots and by radiologists. Rod vision does not give any information about color; it is highly sensitive but reports all colors as shades of gray.

The cones are responsible for color vision. They are harder to study because there are far fewer cones than rods. A new technique has finally solved many long-standing problems. A retina is mounted on a microscope stage. A microbeam of light is passed up through a single cone, and the amount of light passing through is measured. By this technique the amount of light of different wave lengths absorbed by cones can be measured. It turns out that there are three distinct types of cones. One type has a peak absorption for light at a wave length of 450 millimicrons, which is blue light. Another type absorbs green light (maximum at 525–535 millimicrons). The final type absorbs red light (maximum about 560 millimicrons).

It is satisfying to find that there are three kinds of cones, since this is a requirement for most theories of color vision. Newton showed that any color of the rainbow can be made by mixing appropriate amounts of three primary colors. The opposite also holds. Any color of the rainbow could be distinguished by a system having receptors for three different colors. The central nervous mechanism that takes the reports from the three receptors and puts them together to determine the color is still unknown. Color-blind people apparently lack one or more of the receptor types. In a common form of color-blindness, the afflicted individuals lack functional red cones. They cannot tell red from gray.

The three examples were chosen to illustrate the major principles governing the operation of sense organs. The major class of sense organs ignored in the discussion was the chemoreceptors. Olfaction is an especially difficult problem because such a large number of different odors can be distinguished from one another. Based on our experience with color vision, we might expect to find a few basic types of receptor in the olfactory system; different smells would be reported by a shift in the pattern of activity in the receptor types. However, recent experiments show that nerve fibers in the olfactory nerve fire in response to many different substances. The differences between the responses of different neurons are mainly quantitative; one fiber will respond slightly more strongly than another to one chemical. The number of receptor types is not known. Possibly each fiber in the olfactory nerve has a unique response pattern. How the central nervous system can interpret such a complicated input signal is a major mystery.

There are also striking variations from animal to animal in the properties of the sense organs which have been discussed. Some of the variations and some additional sense organs will be described as we consider more closely the relation between sensory abilities and behavior.

FURTHER READING

Békésy, G. von, "The Ear," *Scientific American* (August 1957), p. 66.

Eyzaguirre, C., "Excitatory and Inhibitory Processes in Crustacean Sensory Nerve Calls," in *Nervous Inhibition*, E. Florey, ed. New York: Pergamon, 1961.

Loewenstein, W. R., "Biological Transducers," *Scientific American* (August 1960), p. 98.

Miller, W. H., F. Ratliff, and H. K. Hartline, "How Cells Receive Stimuli," *Scientific American* (September 1961), p. 222.

Ochs, S., *Elements of Neurophysiology*. New York: Wiley, 1965.

Telfer, W., and D. Kennedy, *The Biology of Organisms*. New York: Wiley, 1965.

Wald, G., "The Receptors of Human Color Vision," *Science*, vol. 145 (1964), p. 1007.

chapter 5

Sensory Abilities and Behavior

Man is a poor subject for many kinds of biological study, yet he is excellent for measuring sensory abilities. With a cooperative subject, one simply presents stimuli and asks whether they are detected. Or two stimuli can be presented and the subject can be asked whether they are the same or different.

These experiments are much more difficult with other animals. The animal must give some unambiguous response to show whether or not the stimulus is detected.

PIGEON VISUAL THRESHOLDS In recent years elaborate and accurate methods have been devised from measuring the sensory abilities of laboratory animals. To choose an example, let us consider the method of measuring the visual sensitivity of a pigeon. The first step is to allow the pigeon to live in a special experimental chamber. Every day the overhead light in the chamber is made dimmer, until the animal lives and feeds in complete darkness. At one end of the chamber are two plastic targets or keys (Figure 5-1). One is Key A and the other Key B. Above the keys is a small screen, on which a light spot of known wave length and intensity can be projected. The hopper can be opened long enough for the pigeon to pick up a grain of corn.

Training then commences in earnest. The aim is to teach the pigeon to peck Key A when it sees a spot of light and to peck Key B when the light is not seen. At the beginning the light remains off. Whenever the pigeon pecks Key B, the food hopper opens and it can eat a grain of corn.

The next step is to have the light spot turned on. The apparatus is set up so that a peck at Key A has two effects: (1) a shutter closes so the light spot disappears; (2) Key B is activated. Now a peck at Key B opens the food hopper and also opens the shutter so that the light spot reappears. To be fed, the pigeon must wait for the light spot to appear, then peck Key A. The light spot disappears. Now he pecks Key B and the food hopper opens.

As training goes on, the conditions are changed, so the pecking of Key B only leads to food once in a while (the technique will be described in Chapter 6). The point is to establish a condition where the pigeon will peck the keys at a fast rate and never become satiated with food.

The final step is to arrange the setup so that one peck on Key A decreases the intensity of the light spot. One peck on Key B makes the light spot more intense. With a fully trained animal the following sequence of events is typical. The light spot is on and the pigeon pecks Key A. With each peck, the intensity of the light spot goes down. At random times, spaced on an average of once every 20 seconds, a peck on Key A closes the shutter and the light spot disappears. The pigeon immediately pecks Key B. The pigeon has one chance in nine that a peck on Key B will open the food hopper. The peck on Key B always opens the shutter and at the same time increases the intensity of the light spot by one step.

Sometimes the pigeon stops pecking Key A and pecks Key B even though the shutter is open so that the light spot is still projected onto the screen. Why should the pigeon do this? Simply because the intensity of the light spot has fallen below threshhold. The pigeon behaves as though the light was turned off because it no longer sees the light. The pigeon, therefore, pecks Key B. The intensity of the light spot is increased, so the pigeon returns to pecking Key A.

With this automated method, the dark-adaptation curve for a pigeon can be accurately measured. The overhead lights in the chamber

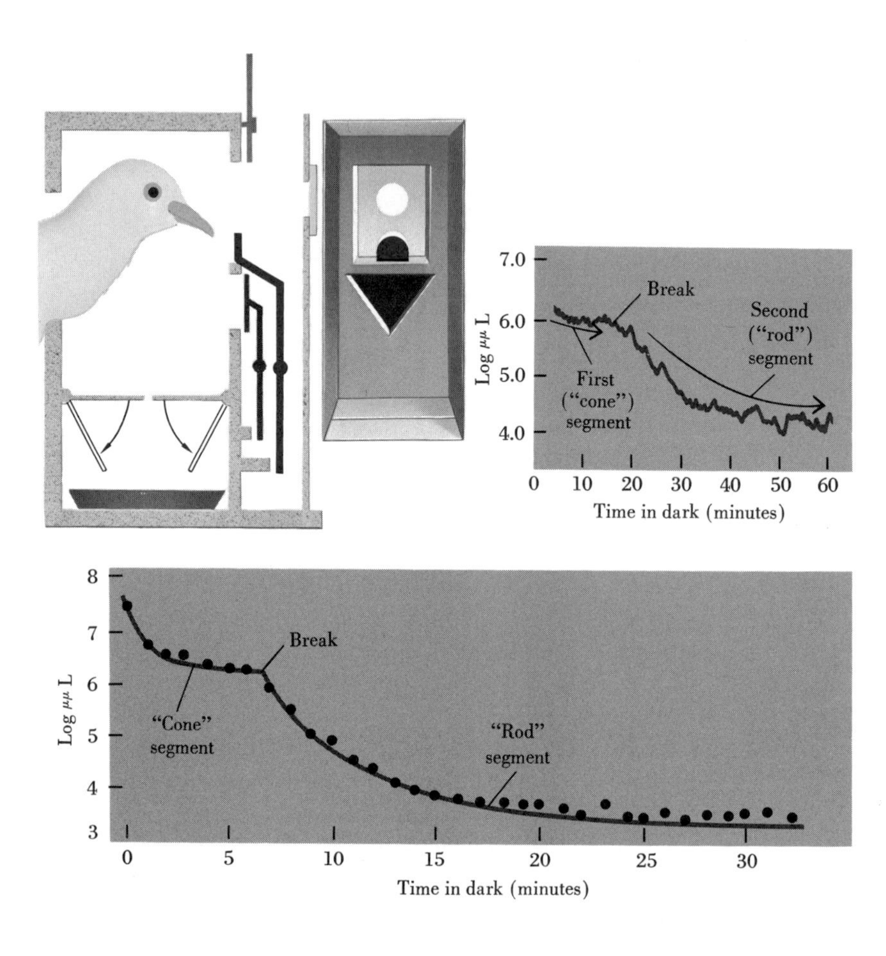

Fig. 5-1 *The apparatus designed to determine the visual threshold of a pigeon. The bird faces an illuminated circle above two keys; their use is described in the text. On the right is the record from an experiment in which the pigeon's threshold was measured during the period after the overhead light in the box was extinguished. The threshold falls in two steps, in the second step the sensitivity is increasing as the rhodopsin concentration of the rod rises. Below are the results of a similar experiment on man, in which the subject tells the experimenter whether or not the light spot is seen. Notice the similarity of this data to that from the pigeon. (Adapted from D. S. Blough, "Dark Adaptations in the Pigeon,"* Journal of Comparative and Physiological Psychology, *vol. 49, 1956, p. 426. Copyright 1956 by the American Psychological Association and reproduced by permission. Carl Allanmore Murchison, Ed.,* The Foundations of Experimental Psychology. *Clark University Press 1929. Worcester, Massachusetts, U.S.A.)*

are turned on to allow the pigeon to become fully light adapted. Then the overhead light is turned off and the light spot is turned on. The pigeon soon shows by its behavior how dim the light spot must become before it is seen no longer. As the animal stays longer in the darkness, the retina becomes more sensitive because the rhodopsin concentration increases and the threshold falls (Figure 5-1).

The sensitivity of the pigeon's eye for light of different wave lengths can be measured by using spots of light of different colors. The results show that the pigeon's spectral sensitivity curve is similar to that of man, except that the pigeon sees better at the violet end of the spectrum and can even detect some ultra-violet light. The difference does not come from the rhodopsin, which is the same in the retinas of the two species. The lens of the human eye contains a substance which absorbs violet light. Therefore, less violet light passes through to the retina. The pigeon's lens is clear. Men who have had their lenses removed have a spectral sensitivity curve almost like that of the pigeon.

COLOR VISION IN BEES Rather different techniques are used to measure the sensory abilities of animals living in the wild. Suitable experiments are difficult to devise, and sometimes the results are conflicting. To choose a famous example, in 1910, a paper was published which concluded that honeybees were color-blind. The conclusion deeply troubled a young German zoologist, Karl von Frisch, who believed that many flowers had evolved shape and color in order to attract the bees who would transfer the pollen. If bees were color-blind, why the magnificient colors?

Von Frisch decided to check the conclusion with a few experiments of his own. He set up a card table near a beehive. On the table was a small dish of sugar water, sitting on a square of blue cardboard. After a while, bees visited the table, sucked up the sugar water and carried it off to the hive. They made trip after trip to the rich source of food. At the end of the training period the sugar water was removed. Two fresh pieces of cardboard, one red and the other blue, were placed on the table. The great majority of the bees coming to the table landed on the blue square.

The experiment showed that the bees can tell the difference between the red and the blue cardboard. It did not show that they have color vision. Totally color-blind men can easily tell the difference between blue and red cards. Red appears as a very dark gray and blue is much lighter; remember that rhodopsin absorbs red light poorly and blue light well (see Figure 4-10).

Therefore, in the next experiment with the bees he placed the blue card among a whole series of gray cards, ranging from almost white to almost black. A dish was placed on each card, but only the dish over the blue card contained sugar water. After the training period, a whole set of fresh cards was placed on the table. The fresh cards were used as a means of preventing the bees from marking cards with scents. The cards were covered with a sheet of glass, in case the blue ink had an odor the bees could detect. The bees continued to land on the blue card and they did not favor any of the gray cards, proof that bees have color vision.

Bees can also be trained to come to orange, yellow, green, violet, or purple cards. They cannot be trained to come to scarlet, since they cannot distinguish between scarlet and dark gray. Bees are "scarlet blind." Furthermore, bees cannot distinguish orange from yellow or green; to them they are one color. Further experiments were made in which bees were trained to come to various colors projected by a prism instead of to colored cards. These experiments showed that the bees can see ultraviolet light. To them ultraviolet is a color; it is invisible to us.

If bees cannot see scarlet, why have plants evolved scarlet flowers? The answer is simply that scarlet flowers are pollinated by birds.

THE DANCE OF THE BEES

Science is a never-ending study. Experiments which are undertaken to solve one problem lead to unexpected observations and new discoveries. While studying color vision, von Frisch learned about the ability of bees to relay information. He noticed that after a dish of sugar water was first placed on the table, hours or even days passed before the first bee landed to investigate. But once the first bee had sucked up some sugar water and departed, many more bees quickly arrived. Within a short time there were tens or hundreds of bees at the table, all from the same hive as the first scout. It seemed plausible that the scout could communicate to his mates that a new source of food had been found.

Von Frisch, therefore, constructed special observation hives so that he could watch the behavior of scouts when they returned. An assistant sat at the table and marked visiting bees with a dot of paint. It was discovered that when the scout returns from the table to the hive, she first gives much of the sugar water to other bees. She then begins to dance. She turns about, first moving to the right, then to the left, then to the right, and so forth. This is the round dance (Figure 5-2).

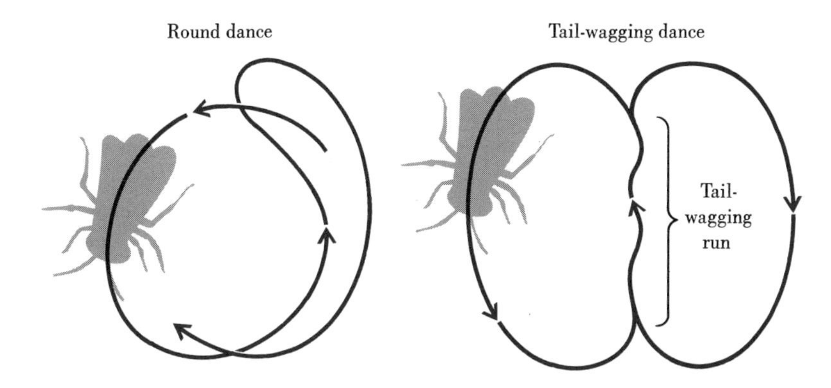

Fig. 5-2 *The dances of the bee. (Copyright 1950 by Cornell University. Used by permission of Cornell University Press.)*

The dance is vigorous and is kept up for thirty or more seconds. The sweeter the sugar water, the longer the dance. The dancer is followed by other bees. One by one, the followers leave the hive. Some of them also reach the table, drink sugar water, and then fly back to the hive to do the round dance. More bees fly out and the food source is exploited fully.

The next step was to place tables at the four points of the compass around the hive. After a forager had found the sugar water at one table and returned to the hive, the number of bees coming to the four tables was counted. There were only chance differences in the numbers visiting each table. The round dance tells bees that there is food near the hive, but does not hint at the direction.

When the scouts find nectar in a flower, they return to the hive with the scent of the flower clinging to their bodies. The bees excited by the round dance leave the hive and seek out the same scent. Scouts who have found a rich food source also mark it with substance they make in a special scent organ. This perfume is attractive to other bees foraging in the vicinity.

In all of these early experiments the feeding table was relatively close to the hive. It was found that if the table was moved further than 50 to 100 meters from the hive, the returning scouts performed a different dance with wagging motions. The following is a description of the dance. The scouts run for a short distance in a straight line, wagging the abdomen from side to side. They then turn completely around, moving clockwise, and repeat the straight segment of the dance, wagging the abdomen as they go. The next turnabout is counterclockwise (Figure 5-2). This wagging dance is packed with information for other bees. In the dance the scout tells both the direction from the hive and the distance to the food source. Distance is correlated with the rate at which the dance is performed. If the food is 100 meters away, a complete turn occurs every 1.5 seconds. If the food is 6000 meters away, a turn occurs every 7.5 seconds (Figure 5-3). The dancer has measured the distance on the outward flight from the hive. We know this because the assistance of a tailwind on the outbound flight can cause the bee to underestimate the distance to the food.

The bee language may also involve sound. During the wagging part of the dance the bee buzzes at about 250 Hz, by vibrating her wings. If the food is nearby, the scout goes through each turn rapidly so that the wagging part of the dance and the buzzing are also short. When the food is far away, the wagging part of the dance and the buzzing are prolonged. There is reason to believe the sound important: if the scout dances without buzzing, as occasionally happens, other bees are not directed to the food site.

Occasionally the dance is done on the landing area in front of the hive. Then the straight-line portion of the dance is performed with the scout facing directly toward the food, pointing the way for the bees following in her steps.

Usually the dance is performed inside the hive, on the vertical honeycomb. Here the dancer cannot directly point to the food. Instead, the straight-line part of the wagging dance is performed at an angle to an imaginary vertical plumb line. This angle is the same as the angle between the sun and the food during the flight out from the hive (Figure 5-4). If the food is reached by flying directly toward the sun, then during the straight part of the dance, the dancer heads directly up. If the food is in the opposite direction from the sun, the dancer heads directly down. If the food can be reached by flying with the sun at right

Fig. 5-3 *The relation between the rate of performing the wagging dance and the distance of the food from the hive. The graph is based on observations by von Frisch of 3,885 dances. (Copyright 1950 by Cornell University. Used by permission of Cornell University Press.)*

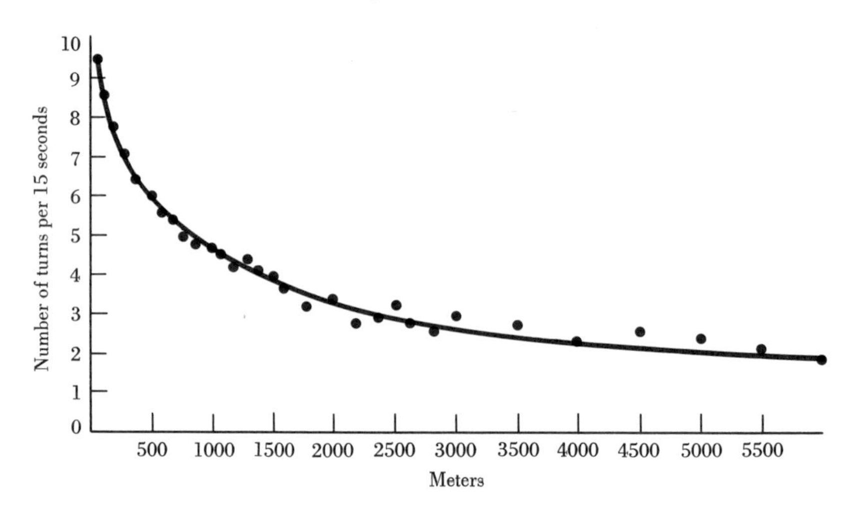

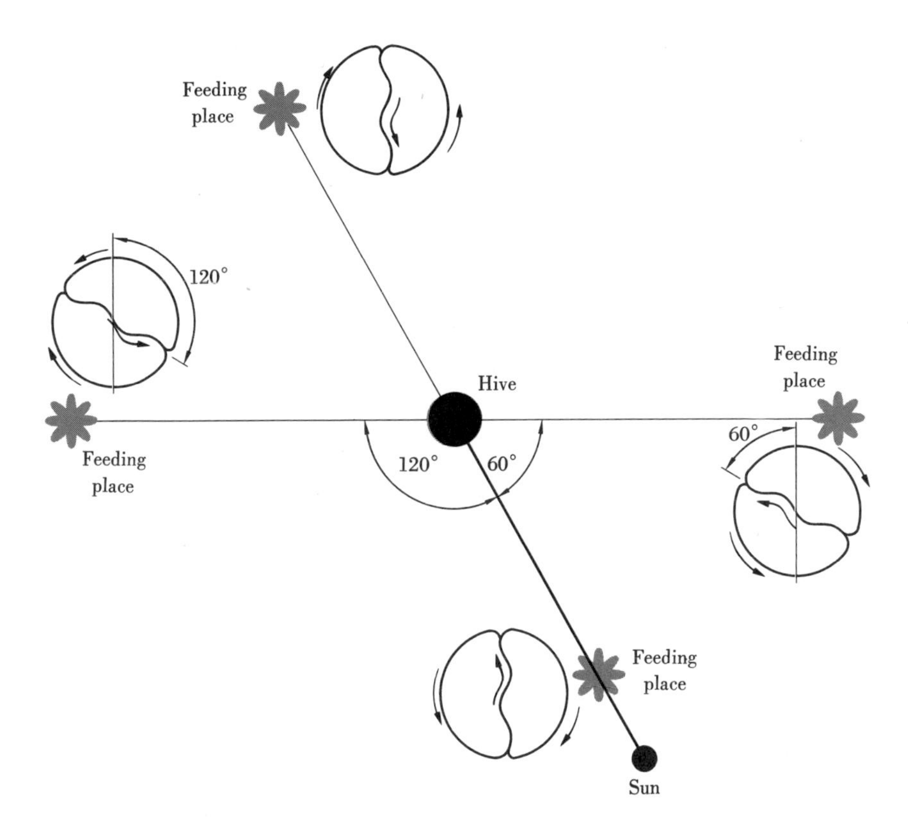

Fig. 5-4 *The orientation of the wagging dance of a bee on a perpendicular comb is determined by the direction of the feeding station in relation to the position of the sun. The direction of the sun is transferred into the upward direction on the comb. (Copyright 1950 by Cornell University. Used by permission of Cornell University Press.)*

angles to the left side of the body, the dancer heads on a line at "three o'clock" from the vertical. The wagging dance is a good indicator to the other bees of the direction of food. When the food is 250 meters from the hive, most of the bees fly out heading within 3 degrees of the correct direction.

In experiments the bees can be restricted to dancing on a comb held horizontally instead of vertically in the hive. The scout then directs the wagging part of the dance straight toward the feeding place. The simplest idea is that the bee now dances directly in relation to the sun, instead of substituting gravity. The difficulty with this interpretation is that the bees dancing in the experimental hive cannot see the sun in the sky. All they can see is a patch of blue sky through the hive entrance. How do the dancers know where the sun stands in the sky? If the hive entrance is covered over, or if a dense cloud conceals the patch of sky visible through the opening, the dance loses organization. The direction in which the bee moves during the straight portion of the wagging dance continually shifts. The other bees are alerted by the dance, but they fly off to all quarters of the compass. Apparently the scout can see something in the patch of blue sky that tells her the direction of the sun.

The light which comes in a direct line from the sun to the point on earth where the observer stands is made up of waves vibrating in all planes perpendicular to the line between him and the sun. However, the light which comes from other portions of the sky has been scattered by particles in the atmosphere; otherwise, it would continue on a straight line away from the sun and would never reach the observer's position. As a result the sky would appear black rather than blue. There is a preferential scattering of the light vibrating in one plane. The light coming from the blue sky is partly polarized in one plane. You can verify this by using a piece of Polaroid, perhaps the lens from a pair of sun glasses. The Polaroid transmits only the light vibrating in one plane. Look through the Polaroid at the sky near the sun. Rotate the piece of Polaroid before your eye. Since the light coming from the sun is not polarized, there will be little change in the amount of light coming through the Polaroid as it is rotated. Now look at the sky away from the sun and again rotate the Polaroid. A good deal of the light coming toward you now is vibrating in one direction. Therefore, as the Polaroid is rotated, the amount of light coming through varies markedly. When the Polaroid is in one position, the sky looks almost black. Now look at another portion of the sky. The light coming from this point is polarized in a different plane, the Polaroid must be rotated to a different position to cut out most of the light. These observations show that if you can detect the plane of polarization of the light coming from a piece of the sky, you can tell where the sun stands. To see whether bees locate the sun by the plane of polarization of the light, a piece of Polaroid is held so that the plane of the polarization of the light passing through it is not changed appreciably. The scouts are restricted to dancing on a horizontal surface. The wagging dance is normal. When the polaroid is turned, so the plane of polarization of the light entering the hive is shifted, the straight portion of the dance is shifted also. Turning the Polaroid further shifts the dance further in the same direction. An essential feature of the bees' behavior is the ability to detect the plane of polarization of the light, a sensory talent we may find hard to imagine. Until the sensory system used by the bee was discovered, there was no hope of understanding this aspect of their behavior.

There is a second problem in the use of the wagging dance to indicate direction. The position of the sun in the sky is continually changing. Suppose that a scout returned to the hive and pointed the angle between the sun and the food at the time when she flew out from the hive. The other bees would be seriously misdirected because in the meantime the sun would have moved to a new position. The dancer actually compensates for the change in the position of the sun at the time she performs her dance. This means that the bee can estimate the time that has passed since the outward flight, and can compensate for the movement of the sun during the interval.

The ability to compensate for the passing of time is especially notable in the behavior of the occasional scout who continues to dance for hours after returning to the hive. As long as the "marathon dancer" continues, she shifts the straight portion of the dance to take into account the movement of the sun. The dancer must be able to estimate the elapsed time and must know also how the position of the sun changes as time passes.

FISH, BATS, AND MOTHS

In many instances, identifying the sensory system used in a particular action is an important advance in understanding the animal's behavior. For example, there are numerous species of fish which live in muddy fresh water ponds. Many of them have evolved electric organs. The electric organ discharges one- or two-volt pulses of electricity at a rapid rate. A current field is generated in the water around the fish. The current is weak and has no effect on other animals. Unlike the high-voltage pulses coming from an electric eel, these pulses are not used for stunning prey.

Suppose, however, that an animal does swim into the feeble electric field. The animal is full of salt solution, which is a better electrical conductor than the water of the pond. More current flows through the low resistance path offered by the animal and the current field around the fish becomes distorted. The fish has a row of receptors sensitive to tiny electrical currents spread along the length of the body. An animal in the field changes the pattern of firing of the fish's receptors. Therefore, the fish can tell that there is a living object in the water nearby. Similarly, if a nonconductor, such as a stone, is placed in the water near the fish, the field will be distorted because less current flows through the region occupied by the stone. The electrical fish can be trained to distinguish between small metal and plastic discs; it becomes visibly disturbed if a magnet is waved past the outside of the aquarium, since this markedly distorts the entire field.

A well-known example of an animal that relies on an unusual sensory ability is the bat. The bat emits high-frequency sound pulses well above the range of human hearing. If an insect is flying in front of the bat, a minute fraction of the sound pulse is echoed back to the bat. The high frequencies are important because only short wave lengths will be echoed from small insects. One species of bat flies at night over tropical ponds and hunts for small fish. The bat detects the ripples on the pond caused by the fish swimming just beneath the surface.

A group of moths which is commonly hunted by bats has hearing sensitive enough to detect the ultrasonic pulses from the bat. When a bat approaches, the moth stops flying in its normal course. Often the moth will "power dive" to the ground, or begin to fly in a zig-zag pattern. Some moths can even generate a high-frequency sound pulse. Perhaps they make sounds which the bat interprets as an echo from a large object in its path.

BIRD NAVIGATION Although numerous experiments have been conducted, the navigational ability of birds has not been explained completely. Homing pigeons released in a strange place will fly many miles back to the home from which they were brought. The mechanism used by the birds to select the proper direction is a matter of conjecture and debate. On cloudy days the pigeons usually stop flying. This fact suggests that vision is probably their most important sensory system.

In a number of studies the pigeons were released and the direction in which they were flying when they disappeared from view was recorded. The studies revealed that a high percentage of birds released on a fair day disappeared heading in the general direction of home. On cloudy days they scattered in all directions and soon settled on the ground to wait for a break in the weather.

Most of the results could be accounted for if the pigeons operated according to the following statement, known as Tunmore's rule: If the sun is higher in the sky than it would be at home at this hour of the day, fly away from the sun. If the sun is lower in the sky than it would be at home at this hour of the day, fly toward it. A bird, acting according to this rule, would start out on a heading within 40 degrees of home. As it flew along, it would encounter familiar landmarks which would help bring it to the loft. Many investigators believe that the birds are far more accurate in choosing direction than Tunmore's rule allows. One suggestion is that the birds estimate their position on the face of the earth relative to home by observing the movement of the sun and estimating, by extrapolation, the position of the sun at the highest part of its arc. By knowing where the sun is at the highest point on the arc, by judging the time of day, and by remembering how the arc of the sun was at home, an animal could theoretically determine the direction of the loft from any point on earth.

It is hard to believe that birds use such complicated mechanisms for navigation, but well-controlled laboratory experiments show that they have a highly developed ability to use the sun as a compass, and an excellent sense of time. The experiments were performed in a circular chamber with an overhead light as an artificial sun. Twelve feeding boxes were spaced around the circumference of the chamber. Birds were placed in the chamber between three and four P.M. every day and trained to get food from the box at 60 degrees to the right of the artificial sun. After the birds were well trained, they were placed in the chamber at different times of the day. The birds did not go to the box at 60 degrees to the right of the sun. They usually went to the box that would be 60 degrees to the right of the sun at four P.M. if the light had moved through the sky in the same direction as the sun. The birds did not learn to go to the food dish located at a set angle to the light. Instead, they learned to go to the box at a certain compass direction, using the sun and the time of day to determine direction.

The birds' clocks can be reset by keeping them on an artificial day-night cycle. For example, birds might be trained to go to the box 60 degrees to the right of the sun when tested between three and four o'clock in the afternoon. After training, the birds might be kept in a closed room, and the light in the room turned on every day at 4 hours after sunrise and turned off 4 hours after sunset. If the birds are retested some days later in the chamber between three and four in the afternoon, they behave as though it is only between eleven and twelve in the morning, routinely selecting the wrong box in relation to the position of the artificial sun. Their time estimate is shifted by the altered day-night cycle.

The extraordinary behavioral problems raised by sun navigation are still less difficult than the question of the navigation of the many species of birds who migrate hundreds or thousands of miles while flying at night. Probably they navigate by the stars. During the migration season, trapped migratory birds appear to orient in the proper direction of travel as long as the stars are visible in the sky or even in a planetarium.

ETHOLOGY AND RELEASERS

In recent years, a vigorous group of European biologists have studied the behavior of animals living in natural or seminatural conditions. They call themselves "Ethologists" and they have sparked a great interest in this kind of investigation. They have experimentally analyzed many instances in which an animal performs a piece of behavior in response to a specific stimulus situation. The experiments often show that in a complicated stimulus situation only a few features are required to elicit the behavior.

As an example, consider the behavior of the three-spined stickleback, a small fish, common to European waters. Sticklebacks live in the sea or in brackish water for most of the year, but in the spring they migrate up the rivers and into the streams. When the male fish arrive

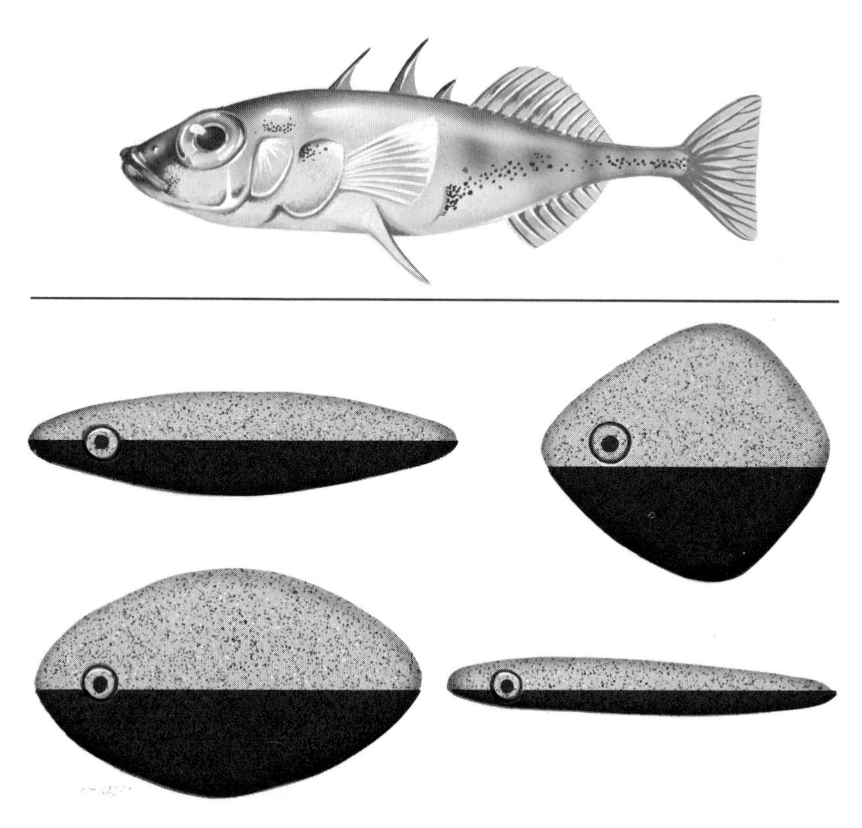

Fig. 5-5 *A model of a male stickleback that is accurate except for the absence of the red belly. This model usually does not elicit territorial defense behavior from other males. Below are a series of models with red bellies and eye spots that do elicit territorial defense. (Adapted from Tinbergen,* The Study of Instinct.*)*

Fig. 5-6 *A male stickleback elicits little reaction if held horizontally in a tube, but if held vertically he produces strong territorial defense behavior by other males. (Adapted from Tinbergen,* The Study of Instinct.*)*

Fig. 5-7 *The model on the right elicits courting behavior from male sticklebacks. The one on the left does not; it lacks the swollen abdomen of an egg-carrying female. (Adapted from Tinbergen,* The Study of Instinct.*)*

in the streams, their bellies are colored bright red. Each male takes up a position in the stream and "stakes out" a territory which he defends from invasion by other males. Female sticklebacks, or other species of fish, can swim into the territory without challenge. Another male, entering the territory, will be attacked.

How do male sticklebacks recognize one another? An Ethologist named Tinbergen answered this question by making a series of models having some of the characteristics of male fish, and maneuvering each model like a submerged puppet into a territory. An accurate model of a male fish, lacking only the red coloration of the belly, is allowed into the territory without protest. But various models—with shapes ranging from cigars to plates—can elicit territorial defense if they feature an eye and a red belly (Figure 5-5). The red belly is called a "releaser" for territorial defense.

The movements of the model are also important. When one male stickleback swims into another's territory and is challenged by the resident, the interloper begins to swim with his body held vertically. The posture elicits further demonstrations from the resident. A model held vertically elicits more intense defensive behavior than a model held horizontally. Even a real male stickleback with a vivid red belly calls forth only limited defensive behavior if he is held in a glass tube unable to assume a vertical position (Figure 5-6).

The male stickleback constructs a small tunnel about two thirds of body length in the stream bed. The tunnel will be used as a nest for the fertilized eggs. If a female stickleback swims into the territory, her appearance stimulates the male to begin a dance. The releaser effect of the female can be duplicated by a model bearing little obvious relation to the female except for an eye and a markedly swollen abdomen—the normal female's belly is distended with eggs (Figure 5-7). The male's dance consists of a series of darting arcs, called the "zig-zag dance" (Figure 5-8). The dance may lead the female to "court"; she swims toward the male, inclined slightly upward so that her underside is exposed. The male responds to courting by turning away from the female and swimming toward the nest, "leading" the female. The female follows the male to the nest. The male now "points" with his head

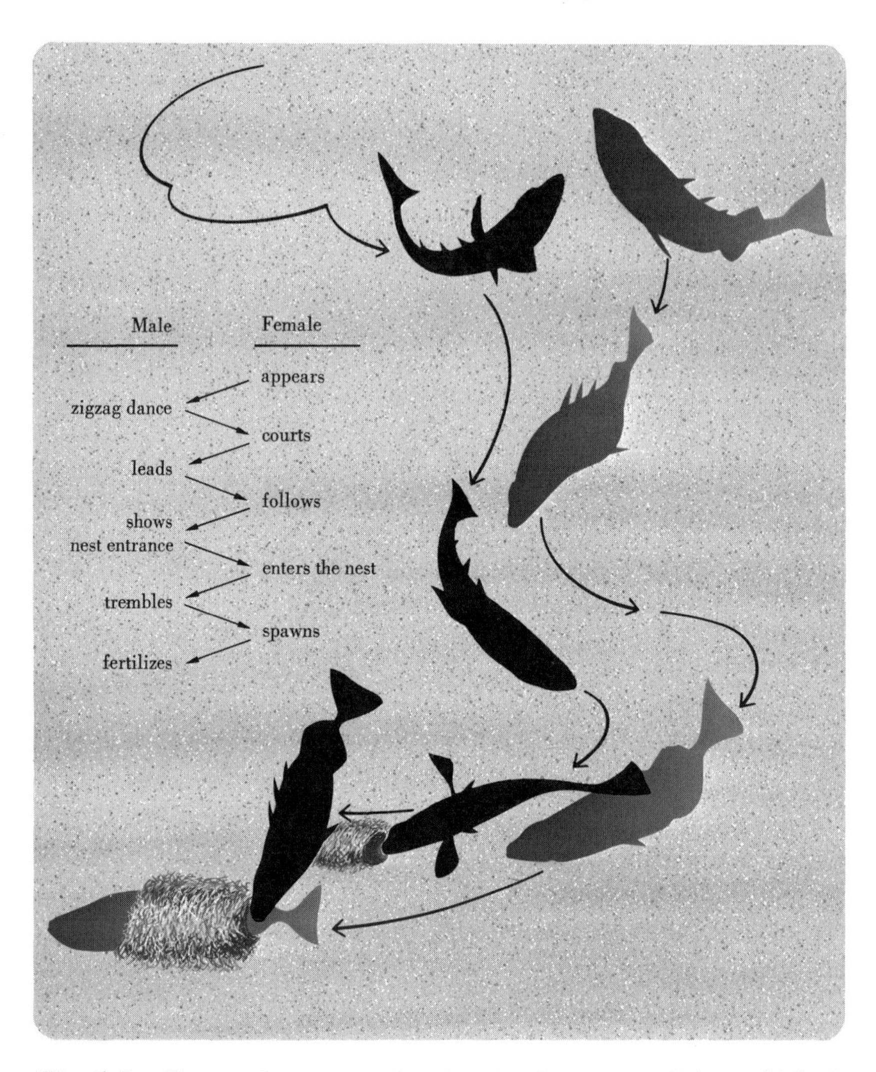

Fig. 5-8 *The usual sequence of actions in the mating of the stickleback. (Adapted from Tinbergen,* The Study of Instinct.*)*

toward the nest entrance. The female enters the nest. As soon as the female is in the nest, the male begins to thrust his snout with quick rhythmic movements at her rump. This behavior is called "trembling." The female then spawns, releasing the eggs into the nest. Spawning can be induced, once the female is in the nest, by mimicking trembling with a glass rod. The eggs provide a chemical stimulus that releases ejaculation by the male. The result is the fertilization of the eggs.

This is a good example of how a chain of releaser-response interactions between two animals can build up a complicated sequence of behavior. However, the descriptions of this or similar behavior chains can be quite misleading unless it is clearly understood that the releaser has a chance, not a certainty, of eliciting the response. When the male is doing the zig-zag dance, there is an increased probability—but no certainty—that the female will court. We are no longer

Fig. 5-9 *A gull is allowed to choose between one of its own eggs and a huge model of an egg. The bird is struggling to roll the model back into her nest; the real egg is ignored. (T. MacAvoy, from* Life *Magazine © Time, Inc.)*

considering spinal animals carefully sheltered from all but the desired stimulus. Free-living animals are barraged with stimuli from all sides, and have a central nervous system which is influenced by many variables. The behavior of the fish during these experiments does not seem like that of an automaton. Courtship may be broken off if one fish or the other simply swims away. The female may not enter the nest; the male may then go back and begin the zig-zag dance once again. At times the male skips ahead in the behavior sequence, or performs some of the behavior when there is no female in the tank at all. The sequence of behavior summarized in Figure 5-8 represents the most probable direction of the behavior, not a rigid, unvarying protocol.

The study of releasers has shown that many animals respond preferentially to models that are gross caricatures of the normal stimulus. For example, birds who nest on the ground will roll nearby eggs into their nests. This behavior normally serves to retrieve eggs accidentally knocked out. A real egg and a model can be placed side by side outside of the nest. The bird is allowed to choose between the two. If the egg is speckled, then a model with larger spots is chosen in preference to the real egg. If the egg has brown spots on a tan background, a model with black spots on a white background is selected instead. Some birds will choose a model of twice normal size, even though it is difficult to roll the massive model into the nest (Figure 5-9). In short, animals often show a preference for supranormal stimuli, that is, stimuli which are more vivid or larger than life.

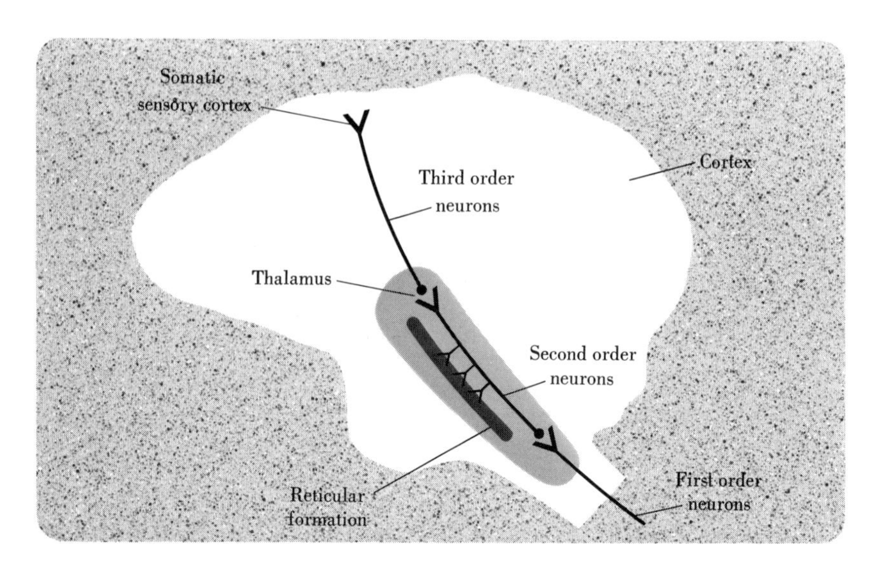

Fig. 5-10 The pathway for somatic sensory messages into the brain. The second order neurons send off a branch into the reticular formation; the third order neurons run from the thalamus to the somatic sensory area of the cortex. (After French, Hernandez-Peon, and Livingston, Journal of Neurophysiology.*)*

SENSORY MECHANISMS OF THE BRAIN

The physical range of stimuli to which an animal will respond is determined by the sense organs. But the elaboration of behavior depends on the processing and selection of sensory information by the central nervous system. The pathways for incoming sensory impulses can be followed step by step with electrical recordings made at different points in the central nervous system.

Consider first the route taken by impulses from touch receptors of the skin: the somatic sensory pathway. The sensory afferent, or first order, axons enter the spinal cord in the dorsal roots. The axons branch and one branch begins to run upward in the spinal cord as part of a great tract of fibers coming from touch and pain receptors. When the fibers enter the brain stem (Figure 5-10), they synapse with the next series of neurons. These second-order neurons cross over to the opposite side of the brain and continue to run upward until they reach the thalamus. As the axons run through the brain stem, they give off branches which run into the reticular formation. The branches are part of the system for arousing the animal, which will be discussed later. In the thalamus there is another synapse. The third-order neurons run from the thalamus to the cerebral cortex. The fibers from the thalamus run to a discrete portion of the cortex, directly behind an infolding

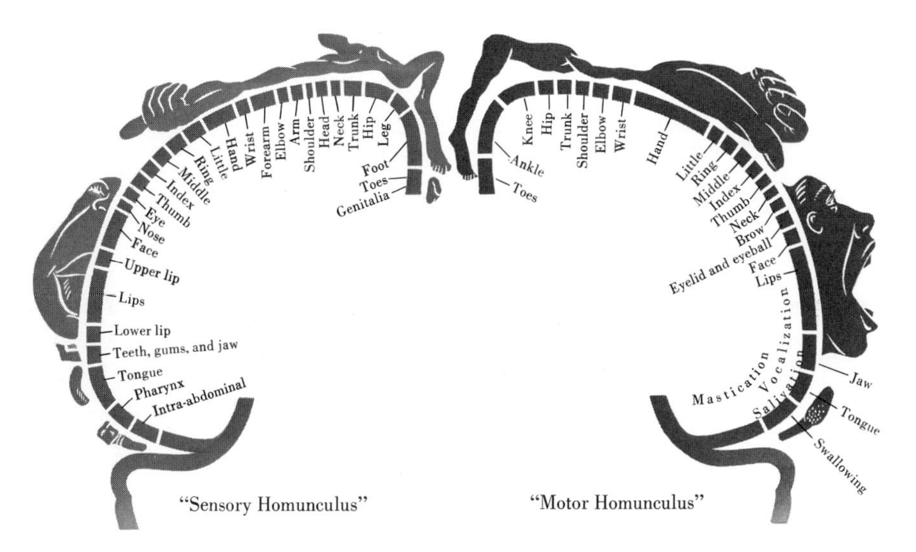

Fig. 5-11 *The localization of function in the motor cortex and in the somatic sensory cortex of man. Notice the large areas devoted to sensation from, and motor control of, the hands and feet. (Reprinted with permission of The Macmillan Company from* The Cerebral Cortex of Man *by Penfield and Rasmusson. Copyright 1950 by The Macmillan Company.)*

known as the fissure of Rolando. This part of the cortex is the somatic sensory area.

There is a topographic separation of function within the somatic sensory area. The localization is demonstrated in man during brain surgery. When the cortex of a patient is exposed, the surgeon must determine the boundaries of the sensory areas. This can be done easily. Cortical surgery is performed with only local anesthesia of the skull and overlying skin, since stimulation of the surface of the brain does not cause pain. The exposed cortex is stimulated point by point with weak electrical shocks. The patient reports any sensation. Stimulation of the somatic sensory area produces a tingling or numbness in one part of the body or another. By moving the electrode, a map of the representation of the body surface on the cortex is obtained (Figure 5-11). The sensory pathway is projected onto the cortical surface as a crude map of the body turned upside down. Regions of the body which are rich in sensory endings—the hands, face, and mouth—are allotted a large area.

The sensory cortex of other animals can be mapped by electrical recording. The projection of the most important sensory regions is always exaggerated. The pig has a large area for the snout, the cat for its whiskers, the monkey for its tail.

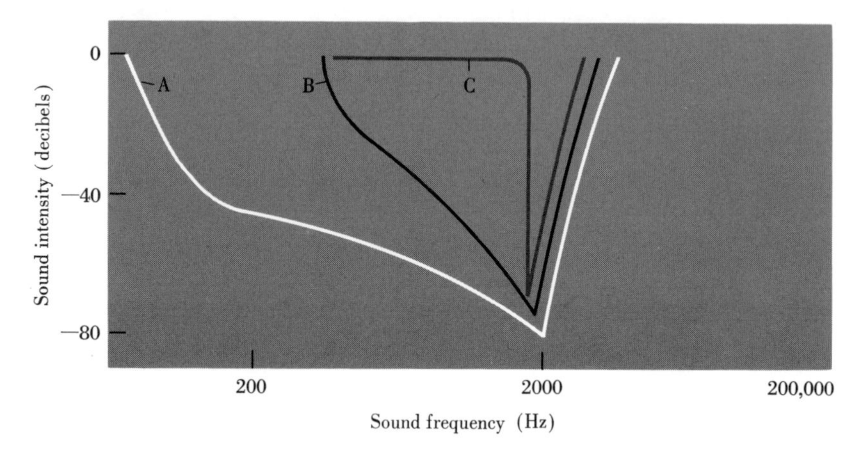

Fig. 5-12 *The intensity of sound required to elicit responses in nerve cells at various steps in the auditory pathway. A neuron in the cochlear nerve (A) will respond to faint sounds over a wide range of frequencies. Neurons in the auditory pathway in the midbrain respond to a more restricted range of frequencies (B). A neuron in the thalamus will fire to faint sounds of only a restricted range of frequencies (C). The sharpening of the auditory message must come about by an interaction between the nerve cells at different steps in the pathway.*

AUDITORY PATHWAYS The neurons from the cochlea run directly into the brain stem. There are several, slightly different pathways to the cortex. Each pathway gives off branches to the reticular system, runs from the thalamus to the cortex, and most of the fibers cross over to the other side of the brain.

The neurons coming from the cochlea respond to a wide range of sound frequencies, which makes it difficult to understand how the animal can distinguish so readily between nearby frequencies. Electrical recordings have been made from neurons at different steps in the path between the cochlea and the cortex. At each step the neurons have been found to respond to a more and more restricted range of frequencies (Figure 5-12). At each synaptic relay there is an inhibitory system which enables the most rapidly firing neurons to inhibit the cells responding less rapidly, thus sharpening the sensory message as it passes upward in the brain.

On the cortex of the cat there are eight distinct auditory projection areas (Figure 5-13). One way to study the function of the projection areas is to remove them surgically one at a time and observe the changes in the animal's behavior. This technique shows, for example, that if the primary auditory projection area is removed from both sides, the cat loses the ability to localize the position of a sound source.

Two groups of investigators set out to test the idea that the auditory projection areas are required for detecting the difference between sounds of different frequencies. A group working in Wisconsin placed their cats in a running wheel. The cat listened to a series of six tones. If the sixth tone was the same frequency as the first five, the cat was not required to move the wheel. If the wheel was moved, the cat was punished with a shock. But when the sixth tone was at a different frequency, the cat had to move the wheel or receive a shock. Nine out of ten cats learned this trick after about 600 trials. Once they reached this level of performance, all of their auditory projection areas were removed. When retested in the wheel, the animals were unable to do the trick. They were given 1500 trials, but they could not relearn. The reasonable conclusion is that the cortical areas are needed for frequency discrimination.

A group in Chicago studied the same question, using a box divided into two sections by a central partition. The partition had a swinging door which was normally locked. The cat heard a steady series of notes at one frequency. Suddenly a second note was added, which alternated with the first. At the same time the door latch was opened, so that the cat could jump through the door to the other side of the box. The two notes sounded alternately five times. If the cat had not moved to the

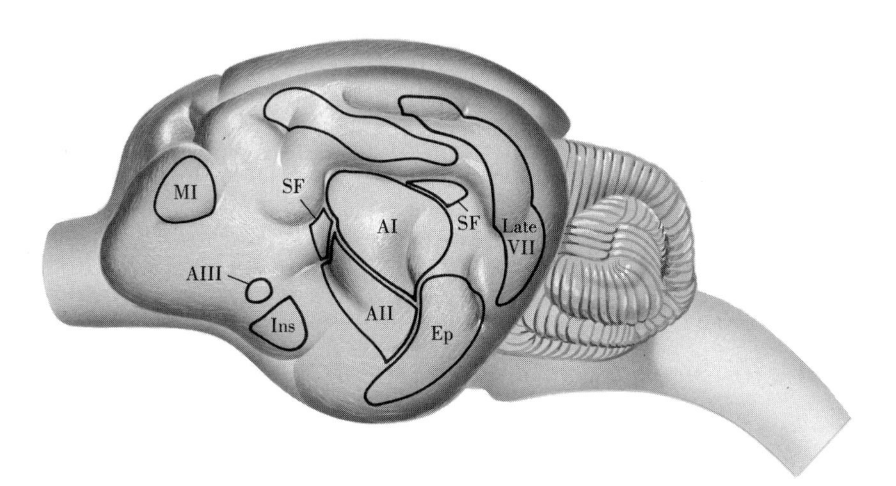

Fig. 5-13 *The auditory projection areas in the cerebral cortex of the cat. The areas are located by searching for sites where an electrical signal is detected whenever a sound is played into the cat's ears. (Adapted from Woolsey, in* Neural Mechanisms of the Auditory and Vestibular Systems, *Rasmussen and Windle, ed., 1960. Courtesy of Charles C. Thomas, Publisher, Springfield, Illinois.)*

other side of the box by the fifth alternation, it received a shock. Cats learned this trick in 120 trials. All auditory cortex were then removed. When retested, the cats no longer performed the trick, but they were able to relearn in 70 trials. These cats could still distinguish between two different tones.

Why did the two experiments give different conclusions? The first step in resolving the conflict was to show that Wisconsin cats behave like Chicago cats when taught in the split box apparatus. The animals are not the reason for the discrepancy. The problem comes from the difference in the complexity of the tasks the cats are required to master. In the running wheel the cats must learn to run when the sound changes. In addition, they must learn not to run when the sound remains steady. When the auditory cortex has been removed, cats cannot learn any task which involves not responding. The moral is that considerable care must be used in interpreting behavioral experiments where there are more variables than are immediately obvious. The experiments also show that a cortical projection is not needed for a cat to distinguish between two different notes, and that other things go on in cortical projection areas in addition to the processing of sensory information.

OPTIC NERVE MESSAGES IN THE FROG

The retina is an outgrowth of the brain. In addition to the primary sense cells, the rods and the cones, there are several types of nerve cells (see Figure 4-9). The final step in the retina is the excitation of ganglion cells, whose axons form the optic nerve. The connections between the rods and cones and the ganglion cells are not well understood, but a great deal of information processing goes on between sense cell and optic nerve.

Electrical recordings can be made from single axons in the optic nerves of the frog. The first experiments showed that there are three functional types of fiber. The stimulus was a tiny spot of light projected onto the retina. Each ganglion cell responds to a light spot in a circumscribed area of the retina—the receptive field for the ganglion cell. The first type of cell fires a burst of impulses when the light spot is turned on in its receptive field; this is the "on" fiber. If the light remains on, the rate of firing falls to a lower level. The second type fires only when the light is turned off; this is the "off" fiber. The final class consists of "on-off" fibers, which discharge both when the light goes on and when it is turned off. The rods and cones are excited only when they are illuminated; consequently, the existence of "off" and "on-off" fibers shows that a good deal of processing goes on between receptor and ganglion cells.

No one realized how much the retina was doing until frogs were shown something more interesting than a flash of light. The frog was placed so that its eye viewed a large sheet of painted plastic. The stimuli are iron silhouettes of different sizes and shapes, held to the sheet by a magnet on the side away from the frog.

By moving the objects around on the sheet, the observers found four classes of ganglion cells. Group I cells respond when there is a sharp boundary between light and dark in their receptive field. The sharpness of the boundary is more important in determing the magnitude of the response than is the contrast between the two shades. If the stimulus is a light spot, the Group I fibers fire when the spot is turned on because there is a boundary between light and dark at the edge of the light spot.

Group II fibers also respond to a boundary in the receptive field. However, the boundary must be curved, and the convex side of the boundary must be the darker. The Group II cell begins to fire when the boundary moves into the receptive field. When the boundary is moved in and then allowed to sit still, the ganglion cell continues to fire. If the background illumination is now dimmed for a moment, or if a shadow is moved over the field, then the cell stops firing, even though the boundary remains at the same spot. If the boundary is then moved slightly, the cell begins to fire again. What kinds of objects will cause Group II fibers to respond in nature? What small, moving dark spots are normally seen by frogs? The answer, of course, is flies and other insects, which make up the frog's food. Group II fibers will detect a fly moving into the receptive field and will continue to report its presence if it lands on a stalk of grass or hovers in one spot. The fly will escape detection only if it remains in one place and a cloud momentarily dims the sun.

The Group III fibers respond to a boundary between light and dark as long as it is moving. They respond if the boundary goes from light to dark to light and also if the boundary goes from light to dark. They are the same as the "on-off" receptors.

Group IV fibers respond when the light is dimmed. A boundary is not needed for their operation. They are the same as the "off" fibers.

It is surprising to think how specialized a view of the external world is reported by the fibers in the frog's optic nerve. Since the Group I and II fibers make up 95 percent of the optic nerve, most of the nerve fires only when there is a boundary in the visual field. Though the visual patterns reported by the retina to the brain of the frog seem limited, the system obviously serves well for the frog. It will be fascinating to learn how the nerve network of the retina analyzes the output of the receptor cells into these four categories.

The ganglion cells of the cat retina have been the subject of another study. The usual type of ganglion cell responds with a burst of impulses to a light spot in the center of its receptive field. A light spot on the periphery of the receptive field inhibits the ganglion cell. There are no special responses to boundaries like those found in the frog.

Recordings have also been made from cells in the visual projection area of the cat cortex. At this step in the visual pathway, cells are found which respond to boundaries, to slit-shaped light patterns oriented at specific angles, and even to boundaries moving in a specific direction. The cat has more general information leaving the retina than does the frog; the cat starts to separate the special attributes of the sensory messsge only at later stages in transmission. The frog can operate effectively with a small nervous system by sifting out the information essential to its well-being at an early stage. The cat takes in a much broader spectrum of information, which is reflected in its richer and more varied behavior. The price paid for versatility is a much larger central nervous system.

FURTHER READING

Blough, D. S., "Experiments in Animal Psychophysics," *Scientific American* (July 1961), p. 113.

Frisch, K. von, *Dancing Bees*. New York: Harcourt, 1961.

Griffin, D. R., *Echoes of Bats and Men*. Garden City, N. Y.: Doubleday, 1959.

———, *Bird Migration*. Garden City, N. Y.: Doubleday, 1964.

Lettvin, J. Y., H. R. Maturana, W. H. Pitts, and W. S. McCulloch, "Two Remarks on the Visual System of the Frog," in *Sensory Communication*, W. A. Rosenblith, ed. New York: Wiley, 1961.

Muntz, W. R. A., "Vision in Frogs," *Scientific American* (March 1964), p. 42.

Neff, W. D., "Neural Mechanisms of Auditory Discrimination," in *Sensory Communication*, W. A. Rosenblith, ed. New York: Wiley, 1961.

Roeder, K. D., *Nerve Cells and Insect Behavior*. Cambridge, Mass.: Harvard University Press, 1963.

———, "Moths and Ultrasound," *Scientific American* (April 1965), p. 94.

Tinbergen, N., "The Curious Behavior of the Stickleback," *Scientific American* (December 1962), p. 22.

Wenner, A. M., "Sound Communication in Honeybees," *Scientific American* (April 1964), p. 117.

chapter **6**

Learning

Many animals change from moment to moment as their behavior is modified by experience. Learning is one of biology's most tantalizing problems, and one that still contains many mysteries. Learning has been subdivided into a large number of categories, but on close examination the lines between many of the classes become blurred so that the systems have only limited utility.

HABITUATION The simplest type of change in behavior as a result of experience is called habituation. A spider is sitting in its web. The experimenter vibrates a point on the web, mimicking the signal set up when an insect is trapped. The spider runs out to investigate the source of the vibration.

Nothing is found and the spider returns to its place in the center of the web. After the stimulus has been given several times the spider no longer rushes out to investigate; it remains in the center of the web. The habituation has not come about by the adaptation of a sense organ, because the spider will come out if the stimulus is applied to a different spot on the web. The spider will also come if the frequency of the stimulus is changed, or if the stimulus is made more intense. Some kind of long-lasting change is produced in the central nervous system.

PAVLOVIAN OR RESPONSE CONDITIONING

The classic conditioning experiment by Pavlov is so well known that the general outlines of the experiment are familiar to the average student. A dog is presented with food, an unconditioned stimulus eliciting salivation. The food is paired for a few times with a neutral stimulus, such as the sound of a buzzer. The previously neutral stimulus then becomes capable of eliciting salivation. A new, conditioned response is established.

The experiment sounds simple, yet it is not that easy to do. The dog must be in a sheltered environment, without distracting stimuli. The buzzer must sound just before the food is presented. If the buzzer follows the sight of the food, conditioning does not occur. The rate at which conditioning takes place depends on the intensity of the stimuli used, the length of the interval since the animal was fed, and the exact timing of the presentation of the unconditioned and the neutral stimuli.

Once the conditioned response is established, it can be extinguished by eliciting the response time after time with the neutral stimulus, without ever reinforcing the response by presenting the food. The number of times the response can be elicited by the neutral stimulus alone depends on how many times the conditioned and the unconditioned stimuli were paired in training.

In most response-conditioning experiments, the effector is a gland or a smooth muscle. Both of these types of effector are controlled in the body by a special efferent outflow, the autonomic nervous system. The autonomic nervous system is anatomically distinct from the somatic motor system controlling the skeletal muscles. Some investigators believe that only responses directed by the autonomic nervous system can be conditioned by Pavlovian methods and that a somewhat different sequence is needed to condition behavior based on the contraction of skeletal muscles.

OPERANT CONDITIONING

Thorndike's puzzle box is less well known than Pavlov's salivating dog, though it undoubtedly deserves an equal place in the history of science. The puzzle box is a chamber shut by a complicated latch that can be operated from inside. A cat is placed in the box. The time the cat needs to escape from the box is measured. The escape becomes faster with each succeeding trial, until the cat reaches a short minimum time for throwing the latch and climbing from the box. Thorndike accounted for the improvement in the cat's performance by pointing out that the cat begins by behaving in many different ways toward the latch. The behavior which is effective in getting the animal out of the box is selected because it leads to a favorable consequence. The principle was called the "law of effect."

Now consider a modern version of the Thorndike experiment. A pigeon is placed in a soundproof box. One wall is transparent, enabling the experimenter to watch the bird's behavior. The bird cannot be watched through the top of the box because an object moving above releases escape behavior, which takes precedence over all other activities. On one wall of the box is a key, which the bird can peck, and a food hopper, which can be opened long enough for the pigeon to pick out a grain of corn. The key is wired to a cumulative recorder, which plots a graph of the total number of times the key has been pecked as a function of time. The apparatus, named after its inventor, is called a Skinner box. The pigeon is deprived of food for some time before it is placed in the box.

When the pigeon is in the box, it will start to do all sorts of things. It may turn around, thrust its head into a corner, stand still for a moment, coo, and then start grooming its feathers. As far as the experiment is concerned, it is unreasonable to describe the behavior as reflex, since there is no change in the environment that can be identified as a stimulus. The central nervous system is at work, selecting between the wide variety of stimuli coming to the animal and producing a single response. Skinner calls these movements that are emitted by the animal "operant behavior." The animal operates on its surroundings. The operant is an expression of the complexity of animals and of their environment, not a basically new kind of behavior. As Sherrington said, "If the animal were merely reflex, its complexity and individuality would make its behavior to the shifting situation of the moment variable beyond all prediction other than statistical." In clinical neurology, operants are called "voluntary" movements.

One of the operations the pigeon in the box is certain to perform sooner or later is to peck at the key. If pecking the key produces no effect, the animal will still peck at it every now and then. Suppose that the peck on the key produces an immediate effect. The food magazine gives a click and opens, the pigeon sees the corn, picks up a grain, and the food magazine closes. Now there is an excellent chance that the pigeon will immediately peck at the key again. If each peck is followed by food, the bird will begin pecking at a rather high rate. The food has reinforced pecking behavior. The reinforcement has brought the rate of pecking from a low level to a high level. This is operant or instrumental conditioning.

Operant conditioning takes place when a movement by the animal is almost immediately followed by a reinforcement, or by the first step in obtaining reinforcement (for instance, the click made by the operation of the food magazine). Then the frequency with which the subject performs the movement increases. In response conditioning, a stimulus that elicits a set response is preceded by a neutral stimulus. The neutral stimulus itself then becomes capable of eliciting the response.

Now suppose that the pigeon has been conditioned to peck the key at a high frequency and the apparatus is set so that a peck no longer leads to reinforcement. The pigeon continues to peck at a high rate at first, and it may take hours before the frequency of pecking falls back to the level found before reinforcement. A particularly well-trained pigeon pecked at the key 7500 times during the first hour after reinforcement ended; during the next two hours, it pecked another 1500 times. The fall-off in the frequency of behavior that is no longer being reinforced is called extinction. The extinction period is often interrupted by bouts of emotional behavior. Pigeons turn away from the key, cooing and beating the air with their wings. Men undergoing extinction may curse, pound the table, or show other signs of annoyance or even rage.

Extinction is an effective way to undo the effects of conditioning. It should not be confused with forgetting. For example, pigeons were conditioned in a Skinner box and then removed without any opportunity for extinction. For the next six years, a period of time equal to half of their life span, the conditioned pigeons were kept away from the Skinner box. When they were finally retested, they immediately began a substantial extinction period.

REINFORCEMENT SCHEDULES

The strength of operant conditioning can be varied by reinforcing according to some regular schedule instead of simply reinforcing every peck. Figure 6-1 illustrates reinforcement at fixed intervals. After a set time interval, the next peck is reinforced. When a reinforcement is given every minute, pecking is at a high rate. The rate

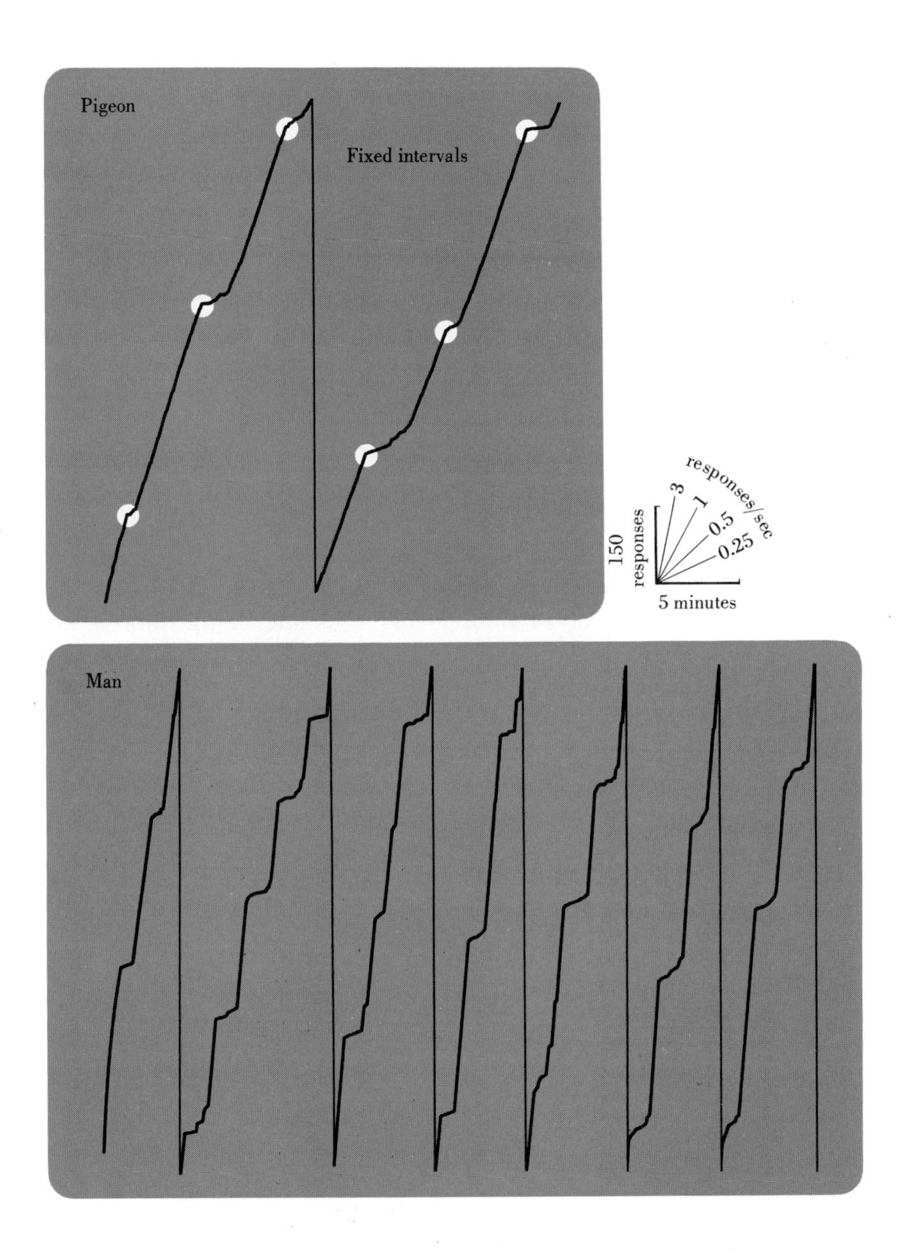

Fig. 6-1 *Performance records for a human and for a pigeon given fixed interval reinforcement. Reinforcement times are indicated by the hatch marks on the record. The vertical lines in the record are produced when the recording instrument has totaled 1000 responses and then automatically resets to zero. After each reinforcement, there is a delay before the rate of response returns to a steady level. The fastest the pigeon performs is about two pecks per second. (Adapted from Skinner,* American Scientist.*)*

is much lower if the interval is five minutes. The behavior established with fixed-interval reinforcement is especially stable; the number of pecks given during extinction is high. (The payment of wages is an example of the use of fixed interval reinforcement in the regulation of human behavior.) After an animal has been given fixed interval reinforcement for some time, the rate of pecking becomes quite slow just after a reinforcement, and then speeds up as the time for the next reinforcement nears.

The rate of pecking can be kept steady by reinforcing at variable random intervals. Pigeons rewarded on a random interval schedule that averages one reinforcement every five minutes behaves with notable steadiness. They peck at a rate of two to three pecks per minute for 15 hours at a stretch. The longest pause in the entire period is less than one minute (Figure 6-2). One reason this experiment works is that with the low rate of reinforcement, the pigeon is not receiving enough food to meet its needs, so there is no risk of satiety.

Another method is to feed the pigeon after a set number of pecks. This is a fixed-ratio reinforcement schedule. If the ratio is kept low, which means that the pigeon has to peck many times for reinforcement, the pecking rate becomes extremely rapid. Apparently fatigue is the only limit on the rate of response. If the animal is kept working under the schedule, the pecking rate falls off just after a reinforcement and then accelerates as the next feeding nears (Figure 6-3).

Extinction takes much longer after a fixed-ratio reinforcement schedule than after variable random interval reinforcement. A pigeon which had been reinforced once every 900 pecks, pecked 73,000 times during the first 4½ hours of extinction.

Fig. 6-2 *Variable interval reinforcement of a chimpanzee. Notice the steady rate of response. The chimpanzee touches its lever on the average of once every four seconds. (Adapted from Skinner,* American Scientist.*)*

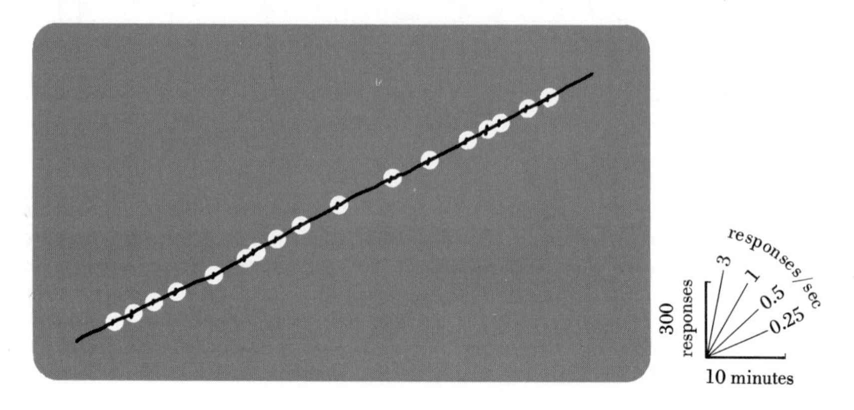

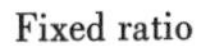

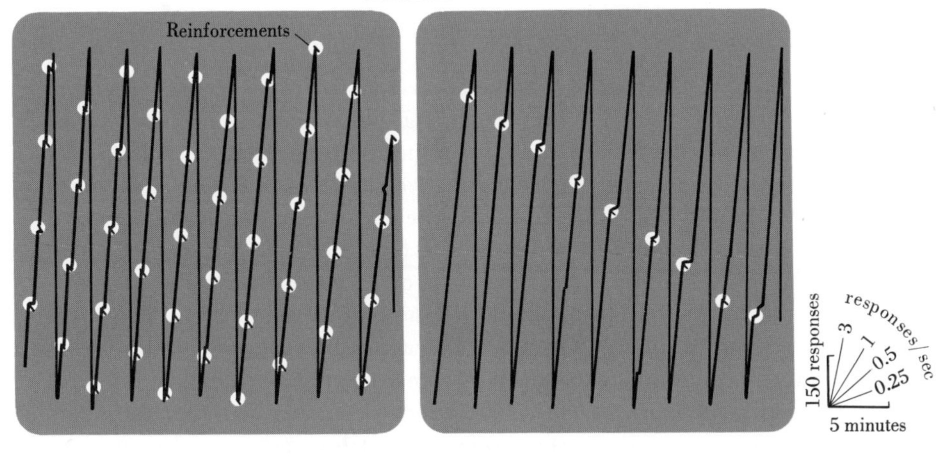

Fig. 6-3 *Fixed ratio reinforcement of a pigeon. Every 210th response is rewarded* (left). *Every 500th response is reinforced* (right). *After each reinforcement the pigeon takes a brief rest. The maximum response rate is about five pecks per second. (Adapted from Skinner,* American Scientist.*)*

Fixed-ratio reinforcement is used in human society in the form of piecework pay. Labor unions generally oppose piecework because of the fatigue produced by working so quickly. In the long run the method is rather inefficient because the worker slows down after the reinforcement and then works up to a fatiguing burst of effort just before the pay-off.

The slow down after reinforcement can be eliminated by using a variable ratio schedule. The animal is reinforced on the average of once every ten responses, or every fifty responses, or whatever number is appropriate. Two responses in a row may be reinforced and then the animal may have to peck several hundred times before the next reinforcement. The chance of being reinforced is the same every time the animal responds. The animal responds rapidly and at a steady rate. A pigeon in a Skinner box will peck 18,000 times per hour and will keep it up for many hours.

A familiar apparatus that works on exactly this principle is the slot machine or "one-armed bandit." The reinforcement schedule is random ratio. The apparatus is notorious for generating a high rate of response. Random ratio reinforcement is the basis of all gambling games and, hence, of an enormous industry.

Why are animals born gamblers? Simply because random ratio reinforcement is the rule of the day. In nature, there are no fixed interval or fixed ratio schedules, aside from the examples in our own society. If animals are to learn under natural conditions, they must evolve so that random reinforcement schedules are effective in molding behavior.

WHAT IS A REINFORCER? As soon as the key role of reinforcement in changing behavior is recognized, it is natural to wonder what events are reinforcing to what animals. So far only limited answers are available because most of the data comes from common laboratory animals like the pigeon, rat, and monkey.

If the animal has been deprived, food and drink become effective reinforcers. Food and drink are most often used in the laboratory because they are easy to manipulate. The chance to breathe might be a good reinforcer, but, so far as I am aware, it has not been used. Sexual contact is reinforcing, though it is rarely used experimentally because of the difficulty in preventing satiation. Grooming by other members of the species may be a reinforcer at least for many social mammals. A fighting cock will peck at a key for the chance to look at its own image in a mirror, or for the opportunity to look at another cock.

Some of the reinforcers of monkey behavior are especially interesting. A monkey kept in closed box will press a lever or perform other tasks for the chance to look at something outside of the box. A view of a bowl of fruit is only slightly effective, the opportunity to see people moving about the laboratory is better, and the sight of another monkey is the best of all. This is a way to measure curiosity, which is such a notable feature of primate behavior. Chimpanzees will spend hours doing simple puzzles, and will do other kinds of work for the chance to solve puzzles. Therefore, puzzle-solving is a reinforcer of chimpanzee behavior. The evolution of these subtle forms of reinforcement must have been one of the important events in the evolution of the primates.

The reinforcers described so far are all doing something for the animal. They are positive reinforcers. Behavior can also be reinforced by removing an uncomfortable stimulus: warming a cold animal, cooling a warm animal, turning off a loud noise, stopping an electric shock. The cold, heat, noise, and shock are described as being negative reinforcers. Animals will work to avoid them.

Some animals can be trained to accept previously novel events or objects as reinforcers. For example, the word "right" is an acquired, or secondary reinforcer of the behavior of students. Monkeys can be schooled so that they are reinforced by awarding a poker chip, which later can be exchanged for a banana. Secondary reinforcers are probably particularly important in the lives of social animals.

DISCRIMINATION Suppose that a pigeon in a Skinner box has been pecking a key for food reinforcement and the situation is changed so that reinforcement is given only when a panel above the key is illuminated. Soon the animal's behavior changes. When the light goes on, the pigeon immediately starts to peck the key.

When the light is turned off, the pigeon stops pecking. The stimulus of the light now controls the pigeon's pecking behavior. The development of the behavior in which the pigeon pecks when the light is on and does not peck when it is off is called discrimination.

Suppose that the light is white, and the pigeon discriminates so that it pecks only when the light is on. If the pigeon is shown a light of any color other than white, it will start to peck, though at a lower rate. This effect is called stimulus generalization. The animal tends to treat related kinds of stimuli interchangeably. If pecking is reinforced only when the light is white, then responses in the presence of colored lights will be extinguished. Soon the pigeons will peck only when the white light is on. The discrimination has been carried a step further.

PUNISHMENT Reinforcement is clearly important in regulating how frequently behavior occurs. But our society often seems to emphasize punishment as a means of changing behavior. Punishment consists of following an unwanted response either by a painful stimulus, or by the withdrawal of a reinforcement. Considering our reliance on punishment, it is surprising to find that there is relatively little experimental work on how to use it effectively.

The first scientific evidence suggested that punishment might be almost ineffective; it came from another experiment by Thorndike. He attempted to train men either by reinforcing correct behavior with the word "right," or by punishing incorrect behavior with "wrong." To his surprise, the reinforcement worked and the punishment proved to be ineffective.

From many experiments with other animals in Skinner boxes, it is certain that the frequency of an operant can be decreased if it is always followed by mild punishment. The punishment must follow immediately after the operant. But if the punishment is discontinued, the behavior will appear once again. After a while, it is difficult to show that the punishment has had any effect whatsoever, particularly if the behavior is reinforced after the punishment is discontinued. It was concluded that punishment is useful only to prevent the appearance of undesirable behavior, and that, when used, it must be continued for the life of the animal.

Then other investigators reopened the question, but they were by no means as gentle. They found that very strong punishments can completely suppress a piece of behavior, with no tendency for the behavior to reappear after an interval. The effectiveness of milder punishments in suppressing behavior declines with repetition; therefore, the intensity of the punishment must be increased or a new punishment must be devised if the animal's behavior is to be regulated by this means.

The use of punishment inevitably produces side effects. Punishment itself is an unconditioned stimulus for changes in the heart rate, the blood pressure, the release of a hormone epinephrine from the adrenal medulla, and for emotions of fear and anxiety. The setting in which the punishment is given is a neutral stimulus which can be conditioned to elicit the emotional response. An animal that has been punished repeatedly will be conditioned to show an emotional reaction to the training box or to the experimenter. Monkeys which are forced to work for six or more hours a day under the threat of a severe electric shock often succumb to stomach ulcers. Control animals receiving the same number of shocks remain healthy.

It would seem reasonable to think that a newly learned piece of behavior, such as pressing a bar for food, would be more susceptible to punishment than acts which are an essential part of the behavioral repertoire of a species. The opposite may be closer to the truth. If a male cat is given a mild shock at the outset of copulation, his subsequent sexual behavior will be markedly diminished. Food intake can also be markedly depressed by mild punishment associated with feedings. There are a number of challenging questions awaiting investigators of punishment. But we may have to wait for the answers because of the reluctance of investigators to undertake studies that inevitably pain their subjects.

The relative ineffectiveness of mild punishment in permanently changing behavior raises a real dilemma for those (for example, parents) who are responsible for controlling human behavior. One alternative is to create harmless situations in which unwanted behavior can undergo extinction. Another technique is to reinforce behavior that is incompatible with the undesirable acts. In other words, it is better to reward a child for cleaning his plate by giving dessert than to spank him for not eating the spinach. Mild punishment of an unwanted act combined with reinforcement of a piece of behavior that requires the use of the same muscles and therefore cannot be combined with the unwanted act is quite effective in training animals, and this method is often used in the laboratory.

CHAINING

On first acquaintance, the changes in behavior that can be demonstrated in a Skinner box appear quite limited. It seems to be a way of changing the frequency of behavior, not a mechanism for establishing new, more complicated behavior patterns. Actually, extremely complicated behavior can be shaped by reinforcement techniques. The behavior is built up step by step. Suppose that a rat is to be trained to pull firmly on a string. In the normal course of events, a rat might have to be watched for months before it ever picks up the string and tugs it. The behavior is built up by first reinforcing movements toward the string. When the rat is routinely hovering about the string, the criterion for reinforcement is raised. Now food is given only when the string is touched. Next the string must be pulled, and finally only a strong pull is rewarded.

By this kind of stepwise procedure, a rat named Pliny was taught to earn its living by pulling a string to release a marble from a rack on the ceiling of the cage. Pliny picked up the marble in his forepaws, carried it over to a tube projecting from the floor cage, raised it over the edge of the tube, and dropped it into the hole. This caused a food pellet to drop into a nearby tray. Pliny ate and then started the whole performance once again. A chain of actions had been built, with reinforcement occurring only at the end of the chain.

By the same type of technique, pigeons have been trained to play "ping-pong"; the winner of each point receives food. And, of course, the same methods have been used by generations of animal trainers, who build their acts by patiently reinforcing steps toward the desired behavior. The whip is used during the performance only to impress the audience.

Reinforcement is a powerful way to modify behavior, but there are definite limitations to what can be done. Animals can never be trained to perform tasks for which they lack the sensory or motor equipment. Nor can they be trained to do things which conflict with other, more powerful behavior patterns. To cite one example, for an advertisement a raccoon was to be trained to pick up two coins and to insert them one after the other into the slot of a toy bank. There was little difficulty in training the animal to pick up a coin and to drop it into a box. But whenever the animal had a coin in each paw, it started to rub the two coins together. The animal could not be trained to drop both coins into the box. The rubbing together of the two coins is obviously part of the typical raccoon behavior of washing food before it is eaten. Washing behavior is elicited by the coin in each paw, and the behavior does not undergo extinction with many trials. Therefore, the raccoon never went on to the next step in the trainer's plan.

The chaining together of behavior is clearly seen in some of the other techniques used to investigate learning. Animals learn to run mazes from the finish backwards. They first learn to make the last turn that leads to the reinforcement, then the next to the last turn, and so forth until the entire maze is mastered.

THE ANATOMY OF MEMORY

Learning must change some part of the nervous system. The first step in exploring the neural mechanism of learning is to find out where the change takes place. Comparative vertebrate anatomy seems to give a clear hint of where to look in the central nervous system for

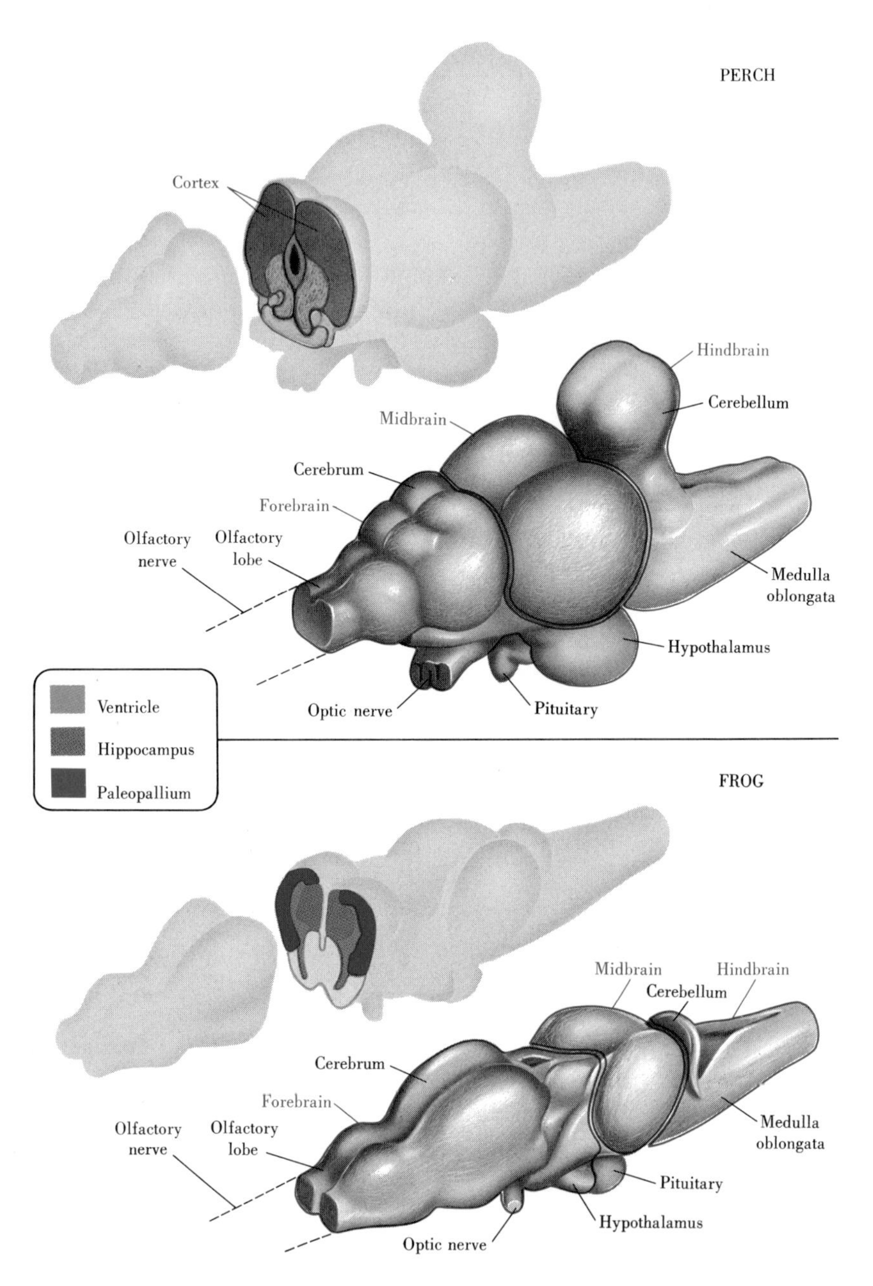

Fig. 6-4 *The brains of four vertebrates. The perch, a bony fish, has a small forebrain. The cortex of its cerebrum has not been homologized with the types of cortex found in other vertebrate classes. In the frog the cerebrum has two distinct types of nerve tissue: paleopallium and hippocampus. The opossum, a generalized mammal, has neocortex making up the larger part of the cerebrum. In more specialized mammals, such as the cat, the extent of the neocortex is further increased by extensive folding. Phylogenetically older types of cerebral tissue are relatively small and have migrated to the bottom surface or to the interior of the forebrain. In the mammals the midbrain is almost completely covered by the forebrain, so that little or nothing of the midbrain is seen in these views. (This figure was drawn from preparations provided by and with the advice of Dr. Douglas Webster of New York University.)*

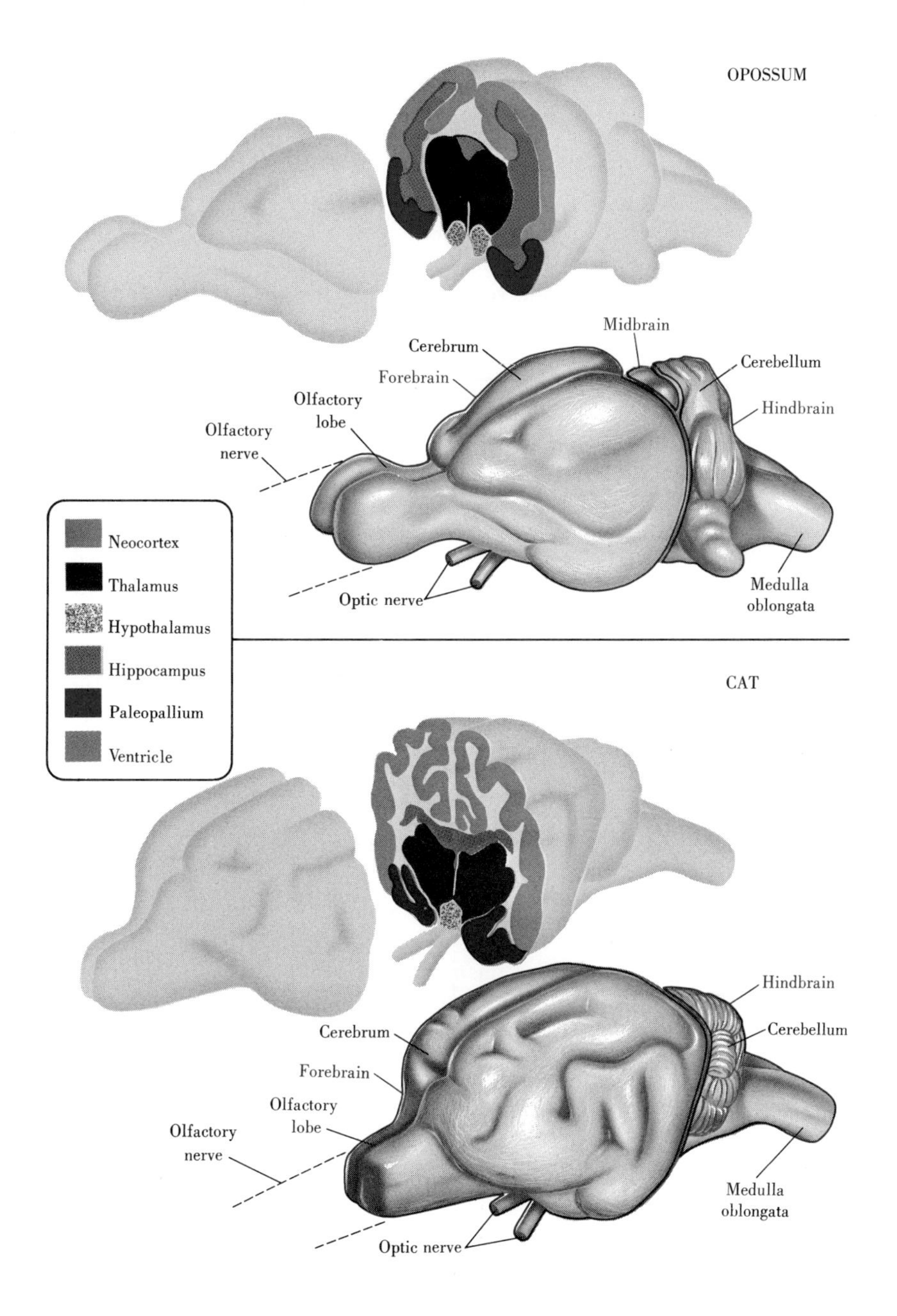

stored memories. In vertebrate evolution, there has been an increase in the capacity to learn. There has been a parallel evolution of certain parts of the brain. The vertebrate brain is formed in embryonic development as a hollow tube. As development proceeds, the brain is divided into three major divisions: the hindbrain, the midbrain, and the forebrain (Figure 6-4). The hindbrain forms the medulla oblongata and the cerebellum. The midbrain remains relatively small; it includes the optic lobe, or tectum. The hindbrain and midbrain are sometimes grouped together and called the brain stem. The forebrain has two major subdivisions: the diencephalon and the telencephalon. The diencephalon includes the thalamus and hypothalamus. The telencephalon forms the cerebral hemispheres, the basal nuclei, and the olfactory bulb. In the course of vertebrate evolution there has been a large increase in the relative size of the forebrain.

The telencephalon of a fish, such as the perch, has a large olfactory bulb but only a small cerebral hemisphere. There is a central cavity or ventricle filled with the cerebralspinal fluid (Figure 6-4).

In the frog the cerebral hemispheres make up a somewhat larger fraction of the brain mass. The gray matter can be divided into three distinct areas: the basal ganglia, the paleopallium or olfactory lobe, and the hippocampus (usually called the archipallium in the Amphibia). The paleopallium and the hippocampus have two or three layers of cell bodies.

Even in generalized mammals, such as the opossum, the cerebral hemispheres make up the greater part of the brain. Except for the basal ganglia, the gray matter is now on the outer surface of the hemisphere, forming a cortex. A large part of the cortex is a new type, the neocortex, which has six layers of cells. In man and in other specialized mammals, the neocortex makes up the greatest proportion of the brain. It has grown so much that the cerebral hemispheres are scored by great infoldings, which increase the surface area devoted to neocortex. A great tract of nerve fibers, the corpus callosum, connects the neocortex on one side with the neocortex on the other side. The paleopallium is confined to a small area on the base of the hemisphere. The hippocampus has migrated inward and downward, so that it is buried within the neocortex.

The clear lesson that seems to come from comparative anatomy is that the evolution of learning ability in vertebrates has been matched by the evolution of an extensive neocortex. Some of the neocortex is used, as we have seen, for sensory projection areas. There is also a motor area, where direct electrical stimulation produces movements of muscles or of groups of muscles (Figure 6-5). In mammalian evolution, proportionately less and less of the neocortex is invested in motor cortex or in direct sensory projection areas. The unassigned portions of the cortex are called association areas.

Sensory messages reach the cortex by way of the sensory projection areas. Motor commands may leave the cortex from the motor area. The rather obvious idea was that input and output were connected by chains of neurons running across association areas. When learning took place, a new pathway was supposed to be laid down through association areas.

This model was so attractive that it took thirty years of investigation to convince almost everyone that it was unsound. Many of the critical experiments were done by Karl Lashley. He began by training

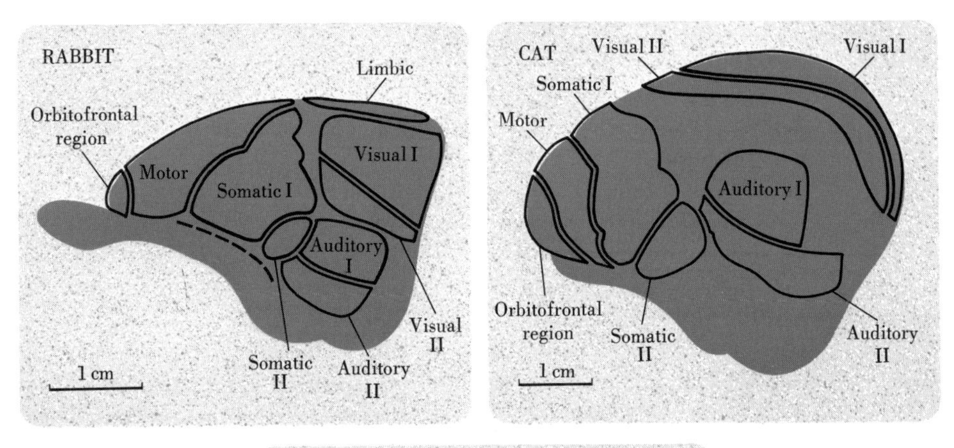

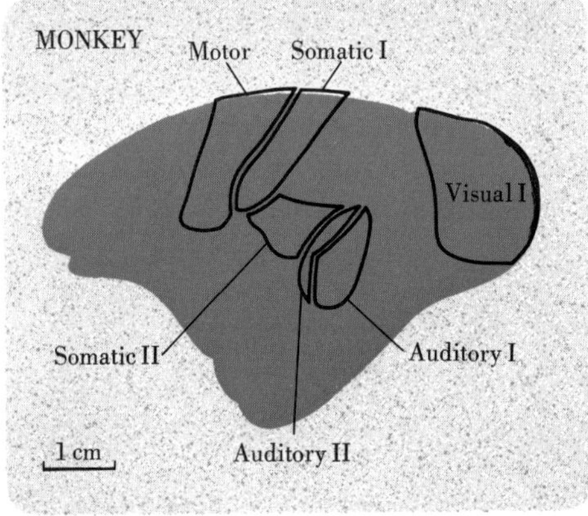

Fig. 6-5 The principal neocortical projection areas and the motor areas of three different mammals. Notice that in the monkey a substantial portion of the cortex is not directly involved in motor or in sensory systems. (Rose and Woolsey, Electroencephalography and Clinical Neurophysiology, *vol. 1, 1949, p. 393.)*

rats to run a maze. The trained animals were then operated, with incisions made all over the cortex, cutting any chain of neurons which might be running from point to point. These animals did not lose the ability to run the maze, and they were just as able to learn new mazes as normal rats. Circuits across association areas could not be shown to be important.

Lashley then removed the motor cortex from monkeys trained to open latch boxes. The animals were paralyzed for twelve weeks after the operation. When they recovered the ability to move, they were retested. They could open the latch box just as well as the unoperated control animals, which suggests that the motor area is not needed for learning.

The next step was a long series of experiments on the effect of the total removal of slabs of the cortex on the ability of rats to learn to run mazes. These experiments showed that the defects in learning ability depend only on how much of the cortex is removed. There seemed to be little difference between one part of the cortex and another, aside from the sensory deficits produced by removing projection areas.

These results produced a widespread skepticism toward the idea that behavior was governed by chains of nerve cells connected to one another by synapses. Some investigators even tried to devise theories which would not require any specific connections between neurons.

However, as work on this problem continued, experimenters began to look carefully for subtle changes in the behavior of brain-operated animals. After all, running a maze is a very complicated task, and it might be difficult to pick out many slight changes in behavior caused by an operation.

The two cerebral hemispheres of the brain are connected by a great band of nerve fibers, the corpus callosum (see Figure 6-6). The corpus callosum was transected in a number of experimental animals and their behavior was tested in mazes. They behaved normally. Here is another example of a large array of nerve cells which seem to have

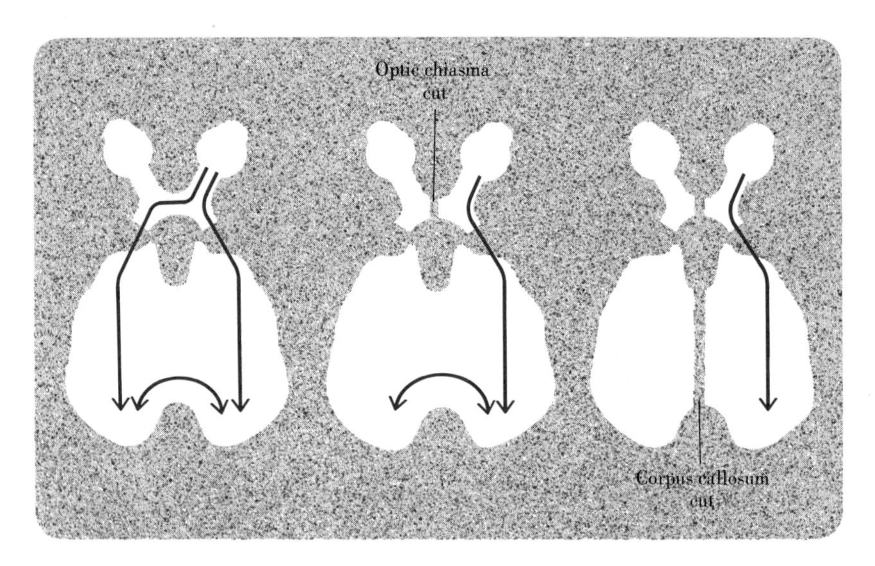

Fig. 6-6 *The neural basis of the split-brain preparation. In a normal animal optic nerve fibers from the eyes run to the visual projection areas of both the right and the left cortex. The visual projection to the opposite side of the body is eliminated by cutting the optic chiasma. The two visual projection areas are still connected by fibers running through the corpus callosum; when these fibers are cut the two sides of the brain, each with an eye connected to it, are split apart from one another. (After Myers, from Glickstein, in Ruch and Patton,* Physiology and Biophysics, *19th edition. Philadelphia, W. B. Saunders Co., 1965.)*

no particular function. Lashley suggested facetiously that the function of the corpus callosum might be mechanical: to keep the two hemispheres from sagging.

In 1959, Meyers and Sperry began to reinvestigate the problem. One potential difficulty in interpreting the experiments is that many sense organs send afferent messages to both the right and the left cerebral cortex. For example, the fibers in the optic nerve from the left eye run to the optic chiasma on the base of the brain. Many of the fibers cross over at the optic chiasma and run to the visual projection area on the left cerebral cortex (Figure 6-6). The rest of the fibers in the right optic nerve stay on the right side of the brain and run to the right cortex. When a cut is made through the optic chiasma, then each eye is connected only to the cerebral hemisphere on the same side of the body. Now, one eye of the cat is covered with a light-tight patch. The cat is taught a visual trick, such as pressing a lever when shown a + sign but not when shown an 0. Once the task is well learned, the patch is shifted to the other eye and the animal is retested. The trick is performed as well as ever, even though this is the first time the visual images have been projected onto this side of the cortex. There is some sort of a mechanism to transfer learning from one cerebral hemisphere to the other.

Other cats were prepared with transections of both the optic chiasma and the corpus callosum, so-called "split-brain" animals (Figure 6-6). These cats are trained in the same way, but when the patch is shifted to the trained eye, they no longer can perform the task. The experience has not been transferred from one hemisphere to the other. The corpus callosum has a very special function, although it takes a well-designed experiment to uncover it.

The experiment works in the same way with monkeys. They can also be used in some more elaborate experiments. The animals are taught in a special experimental box. Polaroid filters are placed in front of the eyes. The filters are arranged so that one eye sees one stimulus. The other eye, at the same time, sees a completely different stimulus. The right side is trained to open a box marked with a + and to avoid a box marked with an 0. The left side is trained to reach for an 0 and to avoid a +. The climax of the experiment comes when the filters are removed, so both eyes see the same stimulus. The monkey is presented with boxes marked with an + and with an 0. The monkey never falters. It begins to open the boxes. One side of the brain is completely controlling the behavior. Sometimes, during a series of tests, there is an abrupt shift and the other side of the brain takes over. This experiment again shows one of the most remarkable properties of the brain, the ability to choose between two incompatible instructions. Perhaps the most important lesson to be drawn from split-brain animals is that

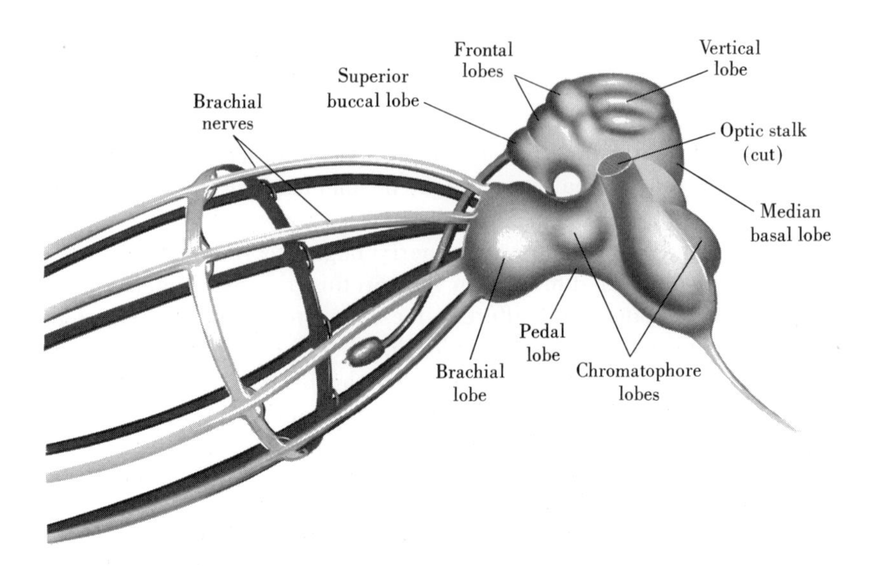

Fig. 6-7 *The brain of the octopus. The most interesting changes in learning are produced by removing the vertical lobe. (Adapted from Boycott, "Learning in the Octopus." Copyright © 1965 by Scientific American, Inc. All rights reserved.)*

an operation can produce subtle yet reproducible changes in behavior.

The behavior of a man with a cut corpus callosum was also studied. The operation was done to prevent the spread of epileptic seizures from one hemisphere to the other. In man, one cerebral cortex is dominant. If the dominant cortex is injured, severe deficits are produced in the ability to use and to understand language. The left cortex of a right-handed man is dominant, and vice versa. The man with the transected corpus callosum is right-handed. He can write easily with his right hand. With his left hand, he is unable to draw a single letter. If he is ordered to move his left leg, he is unable to obey the command, although he uses his left leg perfectly well in all everyday activities. He can use a key with his left hand, but he cannot touch a key with his left hand and name what he holds. Lacking the corpus callosum, he is unable to transfer verbal behavior from the dominant left hemisphere to the right side of the brain.

LEARNING IN THE OCTOPUS

A group of British biologists has been studying the relation between anatomy and learning in octopi for almost thirty years. It is hoped that their research will provide a detailed analysis of how learning occurs in the octopus brain, which contains only about 1×10^8 nerve cells. Octopi can readily be trained to attack and eat a crab, but to avoid a crab accompanied by a white card. If they attack the crab when the white card is present, they are given an electric shock. After the animals are trained to a high level of performance, parts of the brain are removed. The most interesting operation is the removal of the vertical lobe of the brain (Figure 6-7). The operated animals no longer perform the discrimination. If they are retrained on the usual schedule with a trial once every two hours, they never relearn the trick.

If the training is speeded up and the operated octopi are given a trial every few minutes, they learn during the training session to avoid the crab with the white square. When they are retested two hours later, they no longer know the discrimination. The octopus appears to have two kinds of memory systems. There is a short-term memory that retains training for a few minutes. There is also a long-term system, which stores memory more or less permanently. Removal of the vertical lobe of the brain eliminates the long-term system.

LONG- AND SHORT-TERM MEMORY

Mammals also have both long- and short-term memories. The two types can be distinguished experimentally. Rats are given a training session. Their performance improves during the session, so they are acquiring a memory. At varying intervals after the end of the session, the rats are given an electric shock treatment: a powerful electric current is passed through the brain. If the shock is given an hour or more after training, learning proceeds normally. But if the shock is given a few minutes after the end of the training session, it seems to wipe out all of the experience. These animals make little if any progress in learning the task.

Humans receiving electroshock therapy usually have no recollection of the events in the half hour or so before the treatment. And boxers who are knocked out usually have no detailed memory of the last few rounds. Both the electric shock and the knockout blow will simultaneously excite many of the neurons in the brain. These experiments and observations all suggest that memory is acquired in a minimum of two steps. The first step is transitory. It can be eliminated by treatments which simultaneously discharge large numbers of cells in the brain. Therefore, the first stage probably depends on the sustained and integrated firing of aggregations of nerve cells, perhaps impulses circulating in closed chains of neurons. While the first stage is going on, a second stable memory is being laid down in the brain. Once the second step is complete, the memory is fixed and is no longer easily disrupted by shocks or blows.

When the hippocampus and the overlying part of the cerebral cortex (the temporal lobe) are removed from a man for the treatment of epilepsy, there is no interference with old memories. But new memories cannot be established. An article is read, understood, and discussed. But the moment it is put aside, it is forgotten. Even the most dramatic news is forgotten within the hour. The hippocampal system seems to be required for the establishment of new long-term memories.

THE CHEMISTRY OF LEARNING

One of the central ideas of biology is that information is transmitted from generation to generation by using a chemical code, the sequence of bases in DNA. Might not memory also be stored in the form of specific sequences of bases in nucleic acids? Some investigators report that the effects of training can be transferred from animal to animal by injecting RNA extracted from the brain of a trained animal into a naive subject. The effects claimed for the RNA injections are slight, statistical increases in the learning rate of the untrained animals. Even the slight charges are not readily duplicated by other laboratories.

Another way to test the nucleic acid idea is to pretreat animals with inhibitors of nucleic acid synthesis. The antibiotic Actinomycin D inhibits RNA synthesis. Doses of Actinomycin D, which inhibit 85 percent of the RNA synthesis in the mouse brain, do not interfere with learning. So far, the evidence for the RNA theory of memory storage is not compelling.

On the other hand, there are a number of experiments showing that certain inhibitors of protein synthesis prevent the laying down of long-term memory. Goldfish treated with puromycin, an effective inhibitor of protein synthesis, have short-term memory. But they never develop long-term memory.

In mice the effects of recent training are lost — apparently forever — if puromycin solution is injected directly into the region of the brain that includes the temporal cortex and the hippocampus. The performance of the learned task is notably impaired within an hour after the puromycin injection. Three to six days after the training session the injection of puromycin into this region of the brain no longer produces an effect on memory. But if the puromycin is now injected into the remainder of the neocortex as well, then the memory is lost. The site of memory storage seems to spread in the days following training.

Puromycin was chosen as an inhibitor of protein synthesis; however, this may not be the basis of its extraordinary action. Another drug, acetoxycyloheximide, profoundly depresses protein synthesis in the mouse brain, although it does not permanently erase memory.

The key to understanding the chemical changes involved in memory may therefore depend on unraveling the mode of puromycin's action. Puromycin inhibits protein synthesis by being incorporated into an amino acid chain that is being assembled on a ribosome; this causes the premature release of the peptide chain (see *Cell Structure and Function* by Loewy and Siekevitz). Perhaps these abnormal peptides are poisons of memory storage in the brain. The action of puromycin is antagonized by simultaneous treatment with acetoxycyloheximide, which prevents the synthesis of peptide bonds, hence, of any peptide chains. Perhaps when training takes place, an essential messenger RNA (mRNA) is manufactured. The mRNA will direct the synthesis of a protein necessary for preserving memory. When puromycin is present, only short peptide chains are produced, but at the same time the mRNA is used up. Later the drug concentration falls, so that protein synthesis begins again, though now there is no mRNA to specify the synthesis of the proper protein. In mice treated with puromycin and acetoxycycloheximide, all peptide synthesis is halted. This slows the normal breakdown of mRNA, so that when the inhibitors are gone, the synthesis of the specific protein can resume. These ideas can be tested experimentally; the answers will add an important chapter to biology.

The best guess is that the new protein goes into the modification of existing synapses and the formation of new synaptic junctions. The first step in memory is the preservation of the effects of training by the continued activity of large aggregations of neurons. As time passes, structural alterations take place and long-term memory is established. It is difficult to cut memories out of the brain because the connections are widely distributed throughout rather than concentrated in any neat, anatomical package.

The anatomical complexity and the large size of the mammalian brain make the future tasks look extremely difficult. Some of these problems may be side-stepped by finding much simpler preparations that can learn. For example, the thoracic ganglion of a cockroach contains about 3000 nerve cells. The ganglion can be isolated from the rest of the nervous system by cutting the connectives on either side. The ganglion retains sensory and motor connections with a leg on each side of the body. The cockroach is then suspended over a beaker of salt solution. Every time that the roach lowers its leg so that it dips into the solution, the leg gets an electric shock. After a while the animal keeps the leg elevated all of the time, so that it never gets a shock. Has the isolated ganglion learned to keep the leg up? Another interpretation is simpler. Perhaps the electric shock has a direct effect on the neuromuscular system of the roach which makes it hold up its leg. To test this idea, a second roach with an isolated ganglion is mounted alongside the first. The second roach is shocked—no matter what it is doing—whenever the first animal dips its leg into the solution. As the experiment goes on, the second roach shows no tendency to keep its leg up. The behavior of the first roach really is changing because of the consequence of its actions. Anatomically simple preparations like this offer great hope for the future study of the neural changes in learning.

FURTHER READING

Agranoff, B. W., R. E. Davis, and J. J. Brink, "Memory Fixation in the Goldfish," *Proceedings of the National Academy of Sciences*, vol. 54 (1965), p. 788.

Boycott, B. B., "Learning in the Octopus," *Scientific American* (March 1965), p. 42.

Butler, R. A., "Curiosity in Monkeys," *Scientific American* (February 1954), p. 70.

Dethier, V. G., and E. Stellar, *Animal Behavior*, 2d ed. Englewood Cliffs, N.J.: Prentice-Hall, 1964.

Ferster, C. B., and B. F. Skinner, *Schedules of Reinforcement*. New York: Appleton-Century-Crofts, 1957.

Flexner, L. B., J. B. Flexner, and R. B. Roberts, "Memory in Mice Analyzed with Antibiotics," *Science*, vol. 155 (1967), p. 1377.

Keller, F. S., *Learning: Reinforcement Theory*. New York: Random House, 1954.

Lashley, K. S., "In Search of the Engram." *Symposia of the Society for Experimental Biology*, vol. 4 (1950), p. 454.

McGill, T. E., ed., *Readings in Animal Behavior*. New York: Holt, Rinehart and Winston, 1965.

Peterson, L. R., "Short-Term Memory," *Scientific American* (July 1966), p. 90.

Skinner, B. F., *The Behavior of Organisms*. New York: Appleton-Century-Crofts, 1938.

Solomon, R. L., "Punishment," *American Psychologist*, vol. 19 (1964), p. 239.

Sperry, R. W., "The Great Cerebral Commissure," *Scientific American* (January 1964), p. 42.

Thorpe, W. H., *Learning and Instinct in Animals*. Cambridge, Mass.: Harvard University Press, 1956.

chapter 7

Motivation

Suppose that meat juice is placed in the water around a hydra. If the animal has not been fed for several days, the tentacles wave vigorously, the mouth moves, and the threshold for the discharge of the nematocysts goes down. If the animal is well fed, it does not respond at all. The change in the state of the animal shifts the behavior. The animal's motivation has changed. Used in this sense, motivation is the name of a problem, not a single mechanism that regulates behavior.

The level of motivation is often altered by preventing the animal from eating, drinking, or performing some other act. Deprivation makes the animal more ready to respond to some stimuli and less ready to respond to others. The change in responsiveness is referred to as a change in drive. Some biologists have argued that all drives are generated when an animal is tipped away from a normal physiological balance point. For example, if the animal loses water, the concentration of salts in the blood increases. A drive is set up that favors drinking behavior. This is an adequate beginning for discussing thirst; it is far too narrow a starting point for considering drives in general. Attempts to equate all drives with physiological need are doomed to fail.

Remember the example in the last chapter of the monkeys who would work at pressing a lever for the chance to look out into the laboratory. If the animal is kept isolated for a period so that it is deprived of the chance to see what is going on, the behavior becomes stronger. Therefore, "curiosity" in the monkey is a drive.

The unifying idea behind the concept of a drive is not physiological but evolutionary. Animals evolve drives for essential behavior that increases the chance that their genes will be passed along to the next generation. They must have drives for food, for drink, and for oxygen. They will also evolve drives for other advantageous behavior. Many carnivores, for example, have a drive to hunt that is independent of the need for food. Well-fed dogs often hunt. Young cats with a plentiful food supply nevertheless "play" at stalking and pouncing on prey. If a rat is deprived of the chance to run for several days and is then given access to a running wheel, it will run far more than an animal that was not deprived of the chance to exercise. "Activity" is a drive for rats. The strength of a drive is reduced by the performance of a consumatory piece of behavior: eating, drinking, hunting, running are all examples. By this definition, most animals have many different drives.

MEASURING THE STRENGTH OF DRIVES

A number of techniques have been used to compare the strength of different drives. One method is to force the animal to cross a grid that gives it a shock in order to reach food, drink, a member of the opposite sex, an infant, or a running wheel. The intensity of the shock the animal will endure to reach the other side is taken as a measure of the strength of the drive.

A pleasanter technique was used to study the relative strength of the drives of the fighting cock (mentioned in the last chapter) who will peck a key to look at itself in the mirror. The cock is placed in a Skinner box which has three keys. Pressing one key leads to food reinforcement, pressing the second key leads to a drink of water, and pressing the third key opens a panel so he can look at a mirror for a moment. Every day the cock in the box pecks about 100 times for a

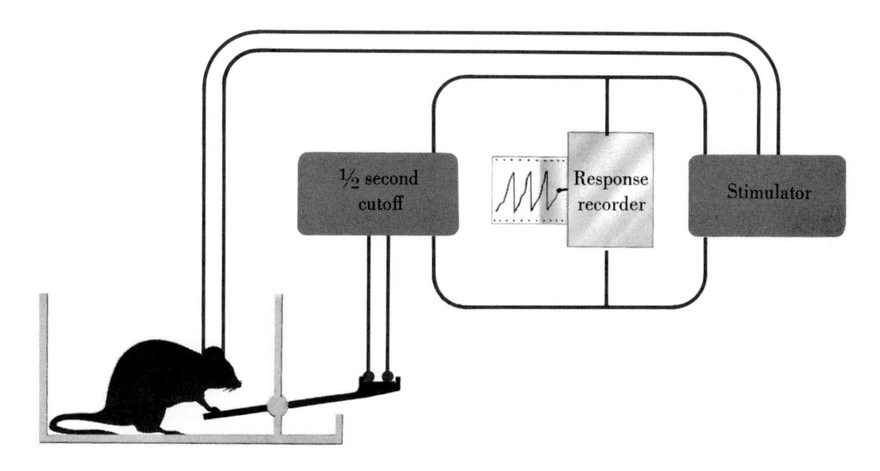

Fig. 7-1 *The design of an apparatus that allows a rat to stimulate its own brain through implanted electrodes. After each press of the lever the brain is stimulated for one half second. (Adapted from Olds and Peretz,* Electroencephalography and Clinical Neurophysiology, *vol. 12, 1960, p. 445.)*

glance in the mirror, about 800 times for water, and about 100 times for food. The numbers give some idea of the strength of the hunger, thirst, and mirror drives in the cock under the conditions of the experiment.

SELF-STIMULATION OF THE BRAIN

In 1954 Olds and Milner tried an experiment that combined physiology and behavior in a totally new way. An electrode was implanted into the brain of a rat. The rat was placed in a Skinner box. The electrode was connected to a stimulator by a thin wire, so the animal could walk about freely in the box. Whenever the rat pushed the lever, the part of its brain around the electrode tip was stimulated for one half of a second. If the electrode was planted in certain selected parts of the brain, the animal pressed the lever more frequently. With one electrode placement rats pushed the lever just as fast as possible, up to 5000 times per hour. They continued lever pressing hour after hour, until they literally dropped from exhaustion (Figure 7-1).

The rats can be taught to perform elaborate tricks by reinforcing their behavior with a stimulus to the proper locus in the brain.

With the electrode in certain areas of the brain, the rate of lever pressing increases when the animal is deprived of food and falls markedly just after the animal is fed. These regions in the brain, therefore, seem to be involved in the neural mechanism for hunger. By similar experiments, other electrode placements involved with thirst and with sex have been mapped.

Many different points in the brain are concerned with hunger; the whole system is not pulled together into one anatomical locus. "Hunger," "thirst," and "sex" points are intermingled in the brain.

A few experiments have been reported in which electrodes were implanted into homologous parts of the human brain. Men push a key to stimulate their brains as readily as rats. None of the subjects reported anything like a vivid hallucination of a delicious dinner or of making love to a beautiful girl. When the brain was stimulated, they experienced a feeling of joy and sometimes a pleasant tickling sensation in the pelvic region. Though the sensations are vague, they are extremely compelling. The possibility that human behavior could be controlled by direct stimulation of the brain is real and terrifying.

If the electrode is implanted into other parts of the rat brain, the animal will push the lever only once. The lever is avoided thereafter. The punishing sites are near tracts believed on anatomical grounds to be part of the central mechanism for pain.

THE LIMBIC SYSTEM

The regions where electrical stimulation has positive or negative reinforcing effects on behavior are in the hypothalamus, the midbrain, and the limbic system. The limbic system is made up of a group of structures in the forebrain and the midbrain. Included are parts of the basal ganglia, the archipallium, the paleopallium, and some transitional regions between these phylogenetically older structures and the neocortex (see Chapter 6, The Anatomy of Memory). The anatomists who worked out the interconnections of the limbic system proposed that it was concerned with emotional responses. There is some evidence to support this idea. To begin with, both reward and punishment, as shown by self-stimulation experiments, always have strong emotional overtones.

Ablation of certain parts of the limbic system produces animals that are abnormally tame and placid. Following this operation, vicious and savage animals, such as the lynx, become gentle and tractable. Electrical stimulation of the same parts of the brain causes the animal to attack any available person or object.

If certain other parts of the lymbic system are surgically removed, the animals become almost unbelievably hypersexual. They will attempt to mate with other animals, regardless of gender or of species, or even with inanimate objects. In the female rat, lesions in the same area cause defective maternal behavior. The operated animals do not make proper nests for the young, nor do they retrieve pups who stray from the nest. The further study of the limbic system should give many insights into the relation between events in the central nervous system and drives, reinforcement, and emotional behavior.

THIRST AND HUNGER

Some drives are related to the necessity of maintaining a balanced physiological state. When a mammal loses water from its body, the blood becomes more concentrated. The change in the concentration of the blood is detected by a receptor located in the hypothalamus. Excitation of the receptor causes two types of response. A hormone is released which promotes the formation of a more concentrated urine, so water is conserved. The animal's behavior also changes, in that it starts to look for water.

The sensory system can be studied by implanting a fine tube or cannula, running from the top of the head down to the part of the hypothalamus containing the receptor. A goat is a good choice for these experiments, since the thick skull between the horns gives a firm site for anchoring the cannula and associated equipment. The apparatus allows the experimenter to inject a drop of concentrated salt solution into the hypothalamus. Whenever the salt solution is released, the goat stops whatever it was doing, runs over to the water trough, and drinks copiously. Drinking can also be produced by electrical stimulation of this part of the hypothalamus. With electrical stimulation, the water which is drunk does not end the stimulus, thus, the goats will drink tremendous volumes. Some goats have taken on 30 percent of the body weight in water during electrical stimulation.

A similar, but more complicated, mechanism regulates eating. If one part of the hypothalamus is destroyed, the operated animals eat almost constantly and become so fat they scarcely move. When a second area is destroyed, the operated animals never eat; they must be force-fed to keep them alive. Presumably, normal eating behavior is produced by the balancing of the activity from these two areas.

There are receptors in the hypothalamus which measure the concentration of metabolites in the blood, and eating behavior is probably governed by this information. There are cells that respond to the glucose in the blood. If the animals are fed gold thioglucose, this substance is selectively accumulated in the receptor cells of the hypothalamus and they are destroyed. The animals then overeat and become very obese. However, the known facts about the regulation of eating cannot be explained by the glucose receptor alone. The mechanism controlling eating behavior remains an important problem in behavior and in public health.

HORMONES AND BEHAVIOR

Some behavior appears only when specific hormones are circulating in the blood. An example was given in the first chapter, where the endocrine system regulating cocoon spinning behavior was described. There are many well-understood examples of hormones regulating sexual and maternal behavior in vertebrates. In both male and female mammals, hormones secreted by the gonads are needed for the development of normal sexual behavior and also for the other behavior which appears in one sex and not in the other. For instance, if young male dogs are castrated, they do not develop normal sexual behavior. They also never begin to raise one hind leg when they urinate. Instead, they continue to squat, like female dogs. If the castrated males are injected with the male sex hormone, testosterone, they acquire secondary sexual characteristics, show interest and ability with the opposite sex, and raise one leg when urinating.

The results are somewhat different if experienced adult male dogs are castrated. They take to squatting during urination, but they often retain sexual behavior. Once animals have experienced sex, it is not easily given up.

When female cats are castrated, the secondary sex organs atrophy and they refuse to accept male animals. Both the secondary sex characters and sexual behavior return if the cats are injected with diethylstilbestrol, a chemical which mimics the action of the normal sex hormone, estrogen. At first it was assumed that the effects on the sex organs came first and set up sensory messages to act on the central nervous system. This idea was tested by applying the hormones directly to the central nervous system. In some experiments, pellets of diethylstilbestrol crystals were placed in the hypothalamus of castrated female cats. The sex organs were unchanged. This shows that the hormone levels in the blood remain low. The female's behavior does change: she readily accepts males. The behavioral effects of the hormone come largely from a direct action of selected parts of the central nervous system.

Many seasonal changes in behavior are triggered by the release of hormones. In coastal streams, the three-spined stickleback may spend the fall and winter in salt water near the sea. In the spring, there is an increased release of hormone by the thyroid gland. The thyroid hormone produces a change in behavior: the fish now prefers fresh water. Therefore, the sticklebacks migrate up the streams to the breeding grounds. Migratory behavior in birds is also stimulated by hormone release. The release of the hormone is triggered, in turn, by the change in the day length.

BEHAVIOR AND HORMONES

The relation between hormones and behavior is a two-way street. Some behavior depends on circulating hormones, and the release of some hormones depends on the behavioral situation. Both aspects are well illustrated by ring doves. If a female ring dove is kept in a cage by herself, she will not lay any eggs. Egg laying can be stimulated by injecting sex hormones. If the female is simply allowed to see a male bird in a nearby cage, then sex hormones are released and eggs are laid.

The same relation is seen in incubation behavior. When a female ring dove is placed alone in a cage containing a nest and eggs, she will not incubate. Incubation behavior develops if the female is injected with the hormone progesterone, or if a male is added to the cage. The two birds start to engage in courtship, and after a few days both birds take turns sitting on the eggs. There are also changes in the female sex organs showing that progesterone has been released. Incubation behavior develops faster if the pair are given a supply of materials so they can also build their own nest. One of the functions of the prolonged courtship behavior of many species of birds may be the stimulation of hormone release.

INTERNAL CLOCKS The world is filled with cues showing the passage of time. There is the daily cycle of light and dark and the monthly phases of the moon. Many animals will behave differently at different times of the day. It seemed reasonable to assume that the animal was responding to the light-dark cycle. However, animals placed under constant illumination, or in constant darkness, at a constant temperature, and with other environmental variables kept as fixed as possible, still show a rhythmic alteration in activity. The rhythm may persist for days or even weeks (Figure 7-2).

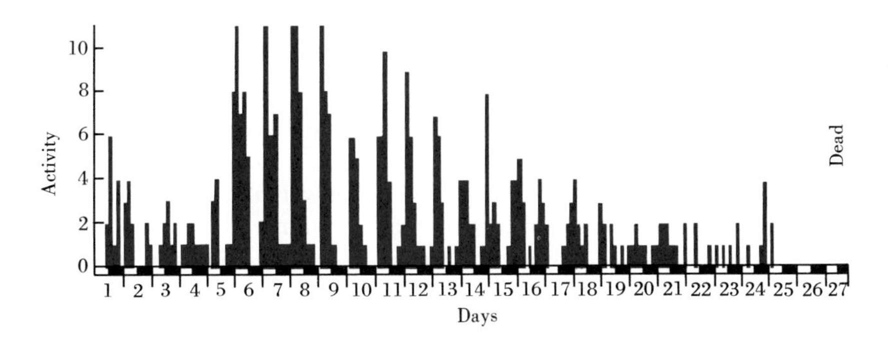

Fig. 7-2 *The activity of a tropical millipede kept in a chamber with constant illumination, temperature, and humidity. There is a peak in the activity of about once a day, until the animal dies on the twenty-fifth day. (Cloudsley-Thompson,* Journal of Experimental Biology, *vol. 28, 1951.)*

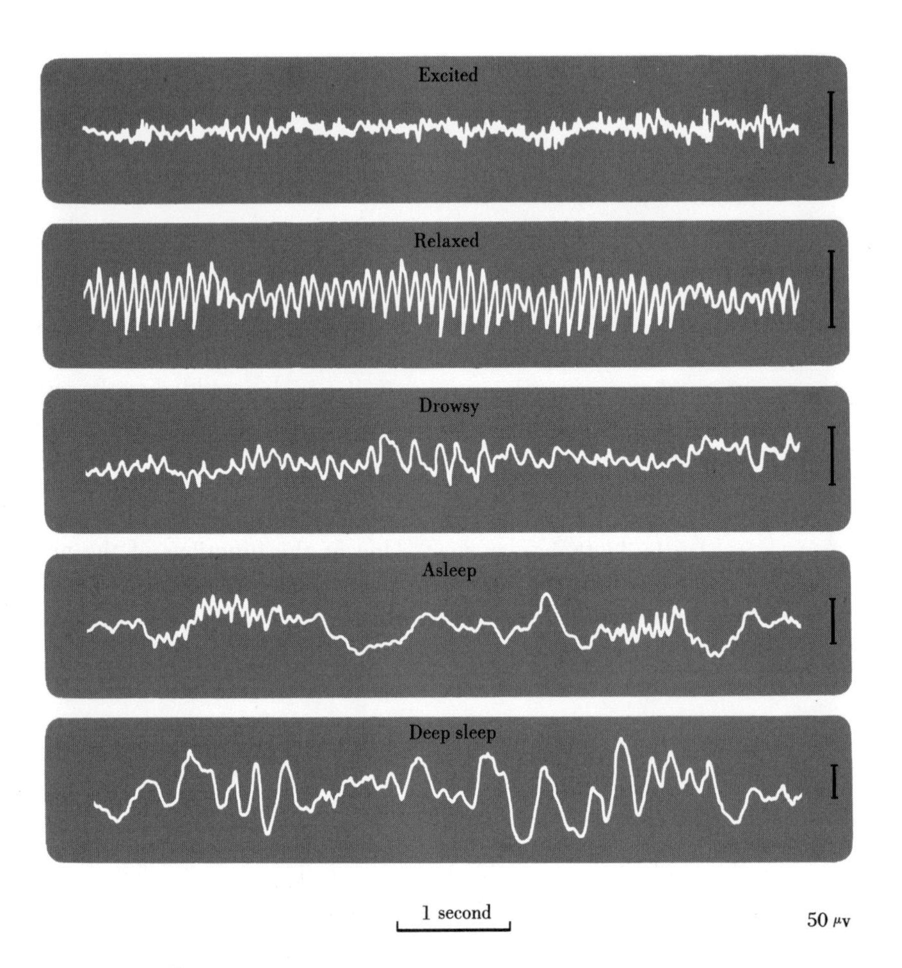

Fig. 7-3 *The electroencephalogram (EEG) of man. (Jasper, in Penfield and Erickson,* Epilepsy and Cerebral Localization, *1941. Courtesy of Charles C. Thomas, Publisher, Springfield, Illinois.)*

When the animal is isolated from the external world, the rhythm is usually not exactly 24 hours. The millipede whose behavior is shown in the figure has a cycle length of about 24.8 hours in constant light, and of about 23.0 hours in constant darkness. Rhythms which persist in constant conditions with a frequency close to 24 hours are called circadian.

Circadian rhythms are commonly found in plants and even in unicellular organisms. A nervous system is not required for their generation. The rhythms can be reset by changes in the illumination cycle, so normally they are kept in phase with day and night. The rhythms are usually insensitive to changes in temperature. In no case do we know how the rhythm is generated and regulated. The prevalence of circadian rhythms in living things helps somewhat in understanding the highly developed sense of time involved in the use of the sun as a compass by honeybees and by birds.

There are also reports that monthly or lunar rhythms are maintained under constant conditions. The experiments were difficult to evaluate because it is easy to confuse random variations with a true rhythm. Recently good statistical techniques for deciding between chance and rhythm have been developed and are being applied to biological data.

SLEEP Many animals alternate every day between periods of action and of inaction. Mammals generally clearly cycle between sleep and wakefulness. The change in behavior is accompanied by an alteration in the pattern of electrical activity which can be recorded from the skull or the surface of the cortex, the electroencephalograph or EEG (Figure 7-3). The EEG of an active, alert man consists of fast, low-voltage activity. When the man relaxes and closes his eyes the EEG takes on a rhythm at a frequency of eight to twelve waves per second. This is the alpha rhythm. In deep sleep the waves are larger and slower. The delta rhythm has a frequency of three to four cycles per second. The EEG allows investigators to tell whether part of the brain is awake or sleeping.

Cats were prepared which had a transection between the midbrain and the hindbrain (Figure 7-4). The EEG shows that the fore- and midbrains, now isolated from the rest of the central nervous system, have the slow activity associated with drowsiness or sleep. The only

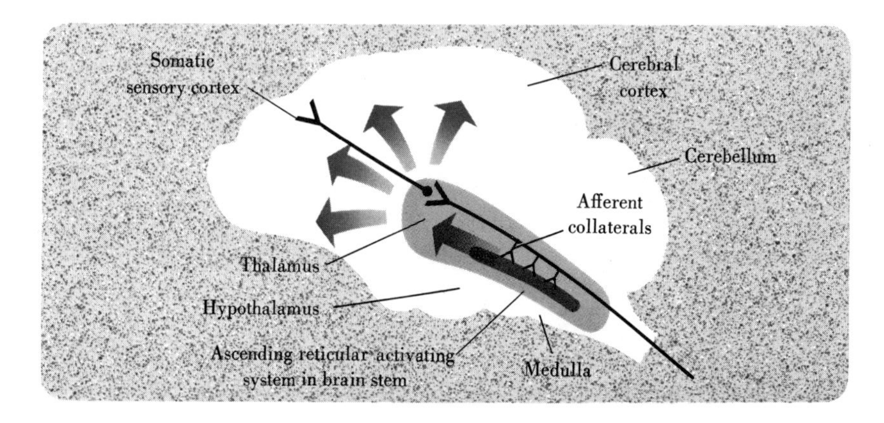

Fig. 7-4 *The reticular system. Impulses enter the reticular formation by way of collaterals from the afferent sensory tracts. There is a pathway from the reticular formation to the thalamus; from the thalamus there is a general, diffuse projection to the cerebral cortex. (After Starzl, Taylor, and Magoun,* Journal of Neurophysiology, *vol. 14, 1951, p. 479.)*

sense organs still connected to the anterior part of the brain are the nose and the eyes. When the animal is stimulated with strong odors, the isolated forebrain temporarily shows a waking EEG.

If the spinal cord is transected just below the medulla, the cats have a waking EEG. Therefore, it seemed likely that some portion of the brain stem was needed to maintain wakefulness. A prominent structure in the brain stem is the reticular formation. All of the major sensory pathways entering the brain give off branches into the reticular formation (see Chapter 4).

The next important experiment was to implant electrodes in the reticular formation of a cat. When the cat began to sleep, the reticular formation was stimulated. The cat immediately woke up. The reticular formation of the normal animal is kept active by sensory impulses coming in on the collaterals from the sensory tracts. When the sensory inflow is cut down, the animal is likely to go to sleep. If the reticular formation is damaged by an experimental lesion or by disease, the animal becomes somnolent. The reticular system acts on the cortex by way of projections from the thalamus.

In man, sleep is interrupted at 80 to 90 minute intervals by periods in which the EEG shows fast, low-amplitude activity. At the same time there are rapid movements of the eyeballs. If the subject is awakened, he reports that he was dreaming. This phase is called REM sleep (for rapid eye movement). Other mammals also have REM sleep. During REM sleep, they show slight movements of the body that also suggest they are dreaming.

CHANGES IN RESPONSIVENESS OF SYSTEMS OF NEURONS

Our understanding of the neural basis of motivation will surely profit from studies on animals with relatively simple nervous systems. Mollusks may be the most useful subjects. In their central nervous systems the nerve cell bodies are very large and the same cells can be identified in every animal. A. O. D. Willows has devised a holder for the sea slug, *Tritonia*, so that single cells in the brain can be penetrated with microelectrodes while the animal is still free to move its body (Figure 7-5). The same microelectrode can be used to stimulate individual neurons in the brain by giving them an electric shock.

The escape reaction is one of the most interesting items of sea slug behavior. The usual stimulus is an approaching starfish—they are vicious predators of sea slugs. The mollusk first bends its body downward, so that it is curved into the shape of an inverted U. This movement pushes it free of the ocean bottom. About two seconds later the

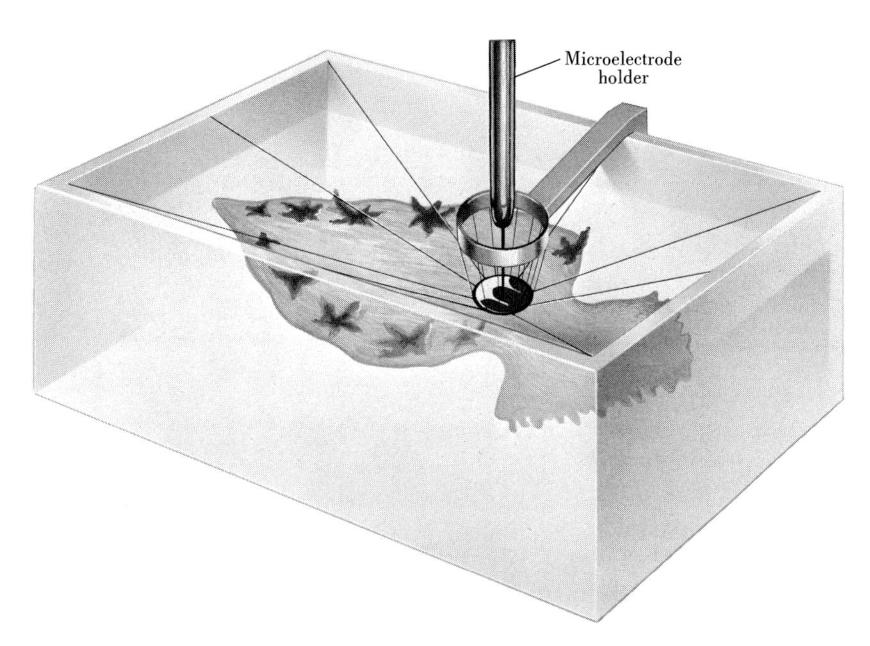

Fig. 7-5 *The method used to stimulate single nerve cells in the brain of an intact sea slug. The area around the brain is immobilized by the special holder, the rest of the animal is free to move. (Adapted from Willows,* Science, *vol. 157, 4 August 1967, pp. 570–574. Copyright 1967 by the American Association for the Advancement of Science.)*

antagonist muscles contract, so the animal now assumes the form of an upright U. The animal can swim a few feet by alternating between the two U-shapes.

The complete escape pattern can be triggered by stimulating certain identifiable, single nerve cells in the brain. One shock will often set off the entire sequence of events. Nerve cells that can produce complicated movement patterns when stimulated are called "command neurons." It turns out that the command neurons for the escape reaction are effective only part of the time; at other times stimulation produces no response whatsoever. There is some mechanism operating in the brain of the sea slug that can change the excitability of the neural mechanism for escape: at some times it is ready to respond and at other times it is not. By studying relatively simple preparations, like the sea slug, it should be possible to discover the mechanism for the change in responsiveness, which is a prime question in the study of motivation.

CONCLUSIONS Animals are not behavior machines which invariably respond in set ways to external stimuli. Many events go on within the animal to alter its responsiveness or even to initiate behavior. These internal changes are lumped together and called changes in motivation. This is a description. It does not mean that one mechanism is always involved or even that one kind of experiment can be used to identify the important variables. Sometimes motivation can be studied by depriving the animal of the chance to make a consumatory response. In other cases, the important variable is the time of day, the season of the year, or the titer of a chemical at a critical locus in the brain.

FURTHER READING

Beach, F. A., ed., *Sex and Behavior,* New York: Wiley, 1965.

Brazier, M. A. B., "The Analysis of Brain Waves," *Scientific American* (June 1962), p. 142.

Cloudsley-Thompson, J. L., *Rhythmic Activity in Animal Physiology and Behaviour,* New York: Academic Press, 1961.

Funkenstein, D. H., "The Physiology of Fear and Anger," *Scientific American* (May 1955), p. 75.

Lehrman, D. S., "The Reproductive Behavior of Ring Doves," *Scientific American* (November 1964), p. 48.

Lorenz, K., *King Solomon's Ring.* New York: Morrow, 1961.

McGill, T. E., ed., *Readings in Animal Behavior.* New York: Holt, Rinehart and Winston, 1965.

Ochs, S., *Elements of Neurophysiology.* New York: Wiley, 1965.

Olds, J., "Pleasure Centers in the Brain," *Scientific American* (October 1956), p. 105.

Tinbergen, N., *The Study of Instinct.* New York: Oxford University Press, 1951.

Willows, A. O. D., "Behavioral Acts Elicited by Stimulation of Single, Identifiable Nerve Cells," *Science,* vol. 157 (1967), p. 570.

chapter **8**

The Development and Genetics of Behavior

One of the questions frequently asked about a kind of behavior is whether it is learned or innate. The question assumes that there are two distinct kinds of behavior which develop in different ways and obey different laws. The innate class is often called instinctive. The two distinct classes of behavior are part of everyday conversation and are used by the man on the street in interpreting behavior.

In spite of its popularity, this classification is neither useful nor accurate. It is not useful because no one can simply watch an animal and reach any valid conclusion about the development of its behavior. Some biologists believe they can recognize innate behavior patterns by looking for acts performed by all members of a species in a rigid and stereotyped fashion. Although this claim does seem persuasive, consider this example. A colony of honey bees was reared in a cellar, illuminated by a stationary lamp. The hive was then moved out of doors. At first the bees were unable to use the sun as a compass for locating food or for dancing. When retested five days later, the sun was used as a compass in the usual way. Evidently some experience with a light that travels across the heavens is needed for the development of the behavior. The behavior is rigid and ubiquitous in the species, but this does not tell us about its development. The members of a species share a common genetic heritage and they usually grow up in similar environments. Both factors work together to develop behavior characteristic of the species.

The division of behavior into learned and innate can be misleading. Even the most painstakingly developed trick, such as teaching a pigeon to play ping-pong, is based on the hereditary ability to learn. On the other side of the coin, subtle environmental events, such as a sun moving through the heavens, may be needed for the normal expression of the genes. To make any estimate of the importance of heredity and of environment in establishing a specimen of behavior, it is necessary to perform a complicated experiment. The experiment will never give an either-or answer; it gives an estimate of the importance of specific experiences in developing a behavior pattern.

At first this might seem to be a serious loss, taking away a familiar and well-worn approach to talking about behavior. On the other hand, the first chapters of this book illustrate that the problems of behavior can be approached experimentally in many ways without ever questioning the origin of the behavior. This chapter will show how rewarding investigations into the development of behavior can be, so long as they do not become part of a foredoomed effort to make an absolute division into two categories which never can exist in isolation from one another.

DEVELOPMENT OF NEURAL CONNECTIONS

The eyeball of an amphibian can be freed in its socket and rotated 180 degrees without damaging the optic nerve. If both eyes are turned upside down, and the frog is then shown a fly, the animal strikes toward a point diametrically away from the target (Figure 8-1). The disturbed vision can be shown in another way also. The animals are placed in the center of a cylinder whose walls are painted with alternating light and dark stripes. The wall rotates slowly in the clockwise direction. Normal frogs or salamanders shift their bodies in the same direction as the moving stripes. Animals with inverted eyeballs shift their bodies in the counterclockwise direction (Figure 8-2).

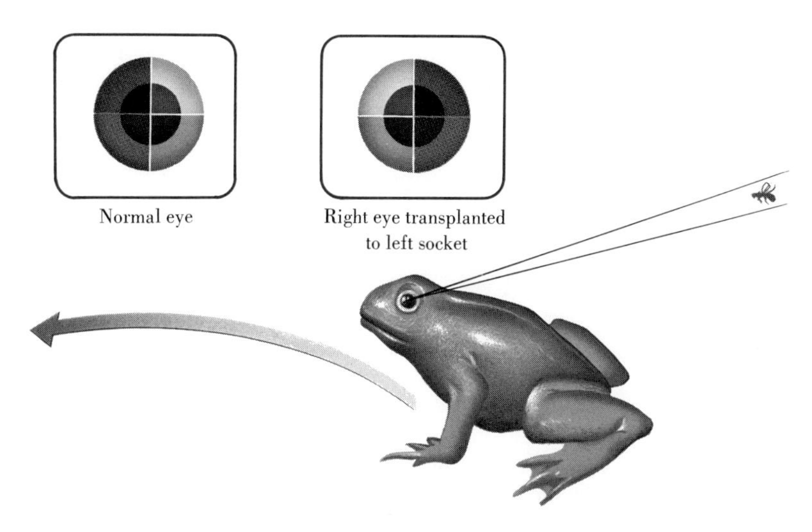

Fig. 8-1 *The behavior of a frog whose eyes were transplanted: a left eyeball was inserted into the right socket and a right eyeball in the left socket. When these frogs see a fly, they strike correctly in the vertical dimension, but 180 degrees away in the horizontal dimension, because the image of the fly is projected on the part of the retina that normally looks forward. (Adapted from R. W. Sperry, in* Handbook of Experimental Psychology, *S. S. Stevens, ed.)*

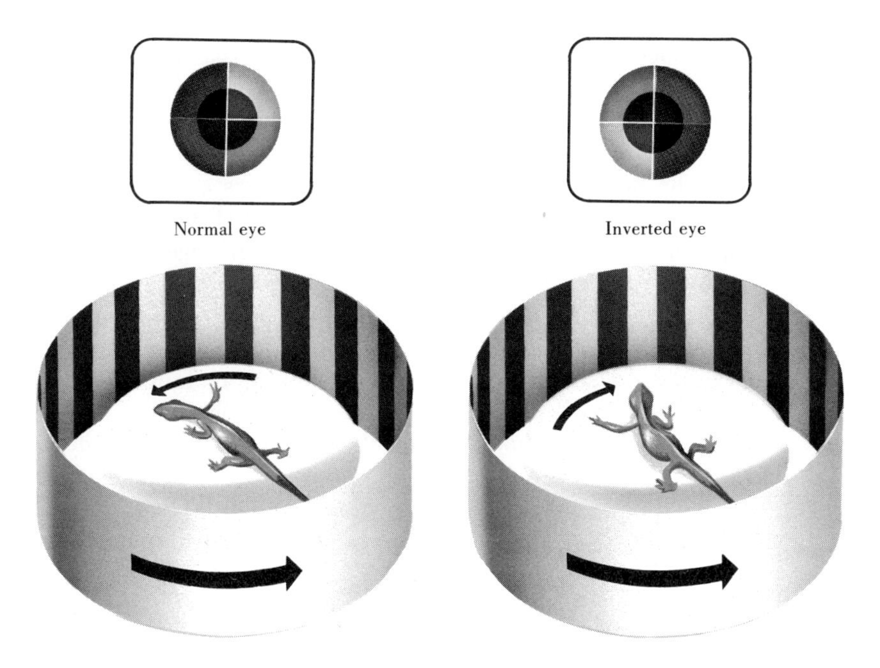

Fig. 8-2 *(A) When a normal newt is placed in the center of a striped drum that slowly rotates, the animal continually shifts in the direction of the rotation. (B) The eyeballs have been removed, turned upside down, and then reimplanted. The animal is given time to recover from the operation. The operated newt turns in the direction opposite to the actual movement of the drum. (Adapted from R. W. Sperry, in* Handbook of Experimental Psychology, *S. S. Stevens, ed.)*

Fig. 8-3 The right and left forelegs of a newt are surgically interchanged. After central connections are established the transplanted limbs still move at the same point in the walking cycle as they would in normal locomotion—even though now the movements push the animal backwards. (Adapted from R. W. Sperry, in Handbook of Experimental Psychology, *S. S. Stevens, ed.)*

The operated frogs never recover normal behavior. This is one of the many behavioral differences between frogs and men. The same experiment is done on man by fitting spectacles which turn the visual image upside down. At first the subjects have great difficulty, but in a few days they adjust well to the inverted visual field. In fact, in spite of the spectacles, the whole world gradually assumes its normal orientation. Once the subject was adapted to the eyeglasses, they are taken off. Now the world appears as if it was turned upside down once again, and a period is needed to readjust to a normal visual field.

The next experiment is to free the frog's eye in the socket, and at the same time to cut the optic nerve. Most of the retina degenerates following the operation, but a new retina then regenerates from what remains. The new ganglion cells grow axons which travel from the eyeball into the optic tectum, which is the visual projection area in the Amphibia (see Chapter 6, The Anatomy of Memory). Once the optic nerve has re-established connections with the tectum, the animals can see again and their vision seems to be quite normal.

Now suppose that the eyeball is taken out, the optic nerve is cut, and the eyeball is turned upside down from its normal position and reimplanted. Again the optic nerve regenerates. These animals strike 180 degrees away from a fly and reverse the normal reaction to moving stripes. This means that the fibers from the retina grow back into the brain and establish the same sort of anatomical relationship as in the normal animal. Apparently enough of the optic nerve fibers grow back to the proper points on the optic tectum to re-establish the old connections.

This interpretation is borne out by further experiments. If part of the optic tectum of a normal frog is destroyed, the animal is blinded in that part of the visual field. If the eye is then removed and turned upside down, the blind spot is also shifted 180 degrees.

We do not know how the axons in the regenerating optic nerve are guided back to the proper points in the optic tectum. The nerve fibers at the point of the cut are disoriented and twisted about. There is no chance that the fibers mechanically follow a path back to the proper points in the tectum. There are about 500,000 fibers in the optic nerve of the frog. Perhaps each of these fibers has a chemical affinity for one of 500,000 points in the optic tectum. The fibers may grow to the tectum at random and continue to grow until by chance alone they hit the proper point. We simply do not understand how it is done. The mechanisms for establishing proper connections during the development of huge numbers of neurons is surely one of the most intriguing problems in biology.

LIMB TRANSPLANTATION

An even more difficult problem is illustrated by experiments in which the entire limb of a larval amphibian is transplanted to another site on the body. Suppose that the two front legs are removed and interchanged: the right leg is moved to the left side, and vice versa (Figure 8-3). The transplanted legs then both face in reverse, toward the animal's rear.

The muscles of the transplanted legs acquire a new motor innervation, and they move in a coordinated pattern when the animal walks. The transplanted right leg is innervated by motoneurons that formerly ran to the left leg, so that the transplant would be expected to move like a left leg. Instead, the transplant moves at the same point in the stepping cycle as a normal right leg, even though its movements now push the animal backward. To account for the result, it seems necessary to suppose that when the motor nerve grows out to the transplant and innervates the muscle, a change is produced in the characteristics of the motoneurons. The change in the motoneurons leads to a readjustment of their connections in the spinal cord. If the motoneuron grows into a transplant and innervates a right biceps muscle, for example, the motoneuron is changed in some way so that it is marked as a right biceps motoneuron. Then the cell body of the motoneuron, back in the spinal cord, acquires some of the central connections normally established with right biceps motoneurons. These experiments should be repeated while using neurophysiological methods for following the establishment of the new reflex connections. Possibly the normal reflex organization of the amphibian spinal cord can account for the results of the experiment in an unexpectedly simple way. Otherwise, the principle will be established that a neuron can be changed by the structure it innervates, and the change will bring about a rearrangement of the neuron's central connections.

DEVELOPMENT OF FLYING IN BIRDS

Long before they begin to fly, young pigeons in the nest make many of the motions of flight. The incipient flight movements gradually give way to short actual flights. For many years naturalists thought that the incipient flight movements were an essential step in the development of flying behavior.

To check this conclusion, pigeons were reared in tight glass tubes, so they were prevented from moving their wings. Their nest mates were free to make incipient flight movements and to take practice flights. Once they were flying rather well, the other birds were freed from the tubes. They were able to fly immediately, and they flew almost as well as their experienced nest mates. The major process in the development of flight is not practice: it is maturation. The newly hatched bird cannot fly, but flying behavior develops with the passage of time, regardless of whether or not the bird can try its wings.

IMPRINTING

The examples given so far are of instances where behavioral development is relatively independent of the environment or even of the consequences of the behavior. The next example shows the importance of a routine experience in the development of normal behavior. Newly hatched ducklings will follow the first moving object they encounter. Usually this is the parent. But with incubator-reared birds it is likely to be a man. If the ducklings begin by following a man, they will continue to follow men in preference to adult ducks. Moreover, as the birds grow up, they behave as if men belonged to the same species. The birds may court a man, or the male birds may treat a man as a sexual rival. When Konrad Lorenz first discovered this performance, he suspected that some distinct mechanism for learning was involved because experience in the first hours of life would produce effects seen years later. Therefore, Lorenz called this imprinting. The term is now used for the learning of some important behavior during a critical period of early life. Imprinting probably does not represent a distinct mechanism; it is a demonstration of the persistence of learning.

Newly hatched birds will also begin to follow moving boxes or a variety of other substitute stimulus objects. The strength of the following behavior is often increased if the stimulus makes some sort of a noise as it moves. Once the young bird starts to follow a particular stimulus object, it always tends to follow it. If the newly hatched bird is not given an object to follow in the first days of life, then it may never take to following, even if the stimulus is its own parent. There is a critical period in the first days, or even hours of life. If following behavior is not established then, it is unlikely to be. The existence of critical periods may well be one of the important rules in behavioral development.

DEVELOPMENT OF BIRD SONG

An ingenious way to study critical periods in development was to investigate bird song. W. H. Thorpe showed that the normal song of the chaffinch consists of three distinct phases. Phase I has four to fourteen notes, usually sung with a crescendo. The mean frequency tends to fall during the series of notes. Phase II has two to eight notes, at about the same pitch, somewhat lower than the notes used in Phase I. Phase III is one to five tones which lead into a terminal flourish.

One of the advantages to studying song is that it can be recorded with high fidelity. The tape recording can be played into an instrument called a sound spectrograph, which gives a chart of the sound frequencies as a function of time. The intensity of the writing on the chart is a measure of the sound intensity. Therefore, a complicated piece of behavior can be analyzed in detail.

Chaffinches can be hand-reared in a soundproof room. After the first few hours of life, these birds do not hear any song except the singing of other hand-reared chaffinches. All of the members of the group reared together sing a similar song. The group song is about as long as the normal chaffinch song, but that is the extent of the resemblance. Listening to the song, one would not think that a group of chaffinches was singing.

Another group of birds was reared by their parents for the first 6 months of life and were then isolated. At this stage of their life, young birds had never sung a note. Some of these birds were kept in a soundproof room containing birds of other species, each singing its own song. Months later, the chaffinches began to sing. They developed a song in which Phases I and II are practically normal; only the final phase is somewhat abnormal. During the 6 months in the wild, the fledglings learned the greater part of the chaffinch song, even though they presumably did not sing a note themselves until much later.

DEVELOPMENT OF MONKEY BEHAVIOR

A few years ago a technique was developed for rearing infant monkeys completely away from their mothers or from a human substitute mother. Under this method the babies are isolated a few hours after birth. They feed from a bottle fixed to the side of the cage. A

Fig. 8-4 *A baby monkey standing on its "terry cloth mother" while it nurses from the bottle on the "wire mother." (Photo by Sponholz for the University of Wisconsin.)*

folded gauze diaper covers the floor of the cage. For obvious sanitary reasons, the diaper must be changed daily. It is not easy to remove the diaper from the cage, since the baby monkey treats the diaper with all of the possessive affection a human infant reserves for its teddy bear. Often the diaper must be torn from the baby.

These observations prompted Harry Harlow and his colleagues at the University of Wisconsin to investigate the relation between the feel of soft materials and the interaction between infant and mother. They first wanted to test the relative importance of feeding and of touching. Therefore, they built two kinds of artificial or surrogate mothers. One surrogate mother had a wooden head, with the outlines of features crudely painted on. The body was a wooden frame covered with wire mesh. A holder for supporting the nursing bottle was built into the center of the "chest." This version was called the "wire mother."

The second model, the "terry cloth mother," was the same except that the body was covered with soft terry cloth (Figure 8-4).

Infant monkeys were placed in a room along with a wire mother and a terry cloth mother. Some infants were always fed from the wire

Fig. 8-5 *A baby monkey flees from a frightening stimulus to its "terry cloth mother." (Photo by Sponholz for the University of Wisconsin.)*

mother; the others were always fed from the terry cloth mother. The two groups of infants drank the same amounts of milk and grew at the same rate. The two mothers were equally effective feeding stations.

But the terry cloth mothers were vastly more attractive to the babies. The infants spent 18 hours a day clinging to the terry cloth mother, regardless of which mother contained the food. The terry cloth mother gave the baby far more than a comfortable perch.

The relationship between the baby and the surrogate mothers can be seen dramatically by exposing the baby to a frightening stimulus. A suitable source of terror is a toy teddy bear, with clockwork that causes it to march forward beating a tin drum. When the marching bear suddenly enters the room, the baby immediately runs to the terry cloth mother. Once the baby is clinging to the mother, the marching bear is regarded with more curiosity than terror.(Figures 8-5 and 8-6).

An infant monkey placed in a strange room containing a few scattered toys is terrified. It throws itself on the floor, clutching its head, rocking its body, and crying in misery and distress. The resemblance between this behavior and the actions of seriously disturbed human children is too close to be missed. Suppose that the wire mother is placed into the strange room along with the infant. This does little good. The baby still cries and huddles, too afraid to explore. But if the terry cloth mother is put in along with the baby, the infant runs immediately to the mother and clings to her. Early signs of distress and fear soon vanish. After a little while the baby leaves the mother and begins to explore the room. From then on its behavior is much like that of a human child in the same situation. Periods of investigation and play are interrupted by trips back to the mother for reassurance. The terry cloth mother is an important source of comfort and security for the baby. Apparently tactile stimulation is vitally important in forging the bond between the baby and its surrogate mother. Warming the terry cloth with a heating pad does not make her appreciably more attractive, so at normal comfortable laboratory temperatures warmth is not important.

Another way to measure the degree of attachment of the babies for the surrogate mothers is to use bar-pressing experiments. Monkeys will press a lever for a view outside of the experimental box. The reinforcing value of the view depends on what the monkeys see; the experimental babies press the lever at a high rate for a view of the terry cloth mother.

Fig. 8-6 *Once the baby is securely clinging to its mother, it regards a strange stimulus with curiosity rather than terror. The baby may even leave the shelter of the mother for brief inspection trips. (Photo by Sponholz for the University of Wisconsin.)*

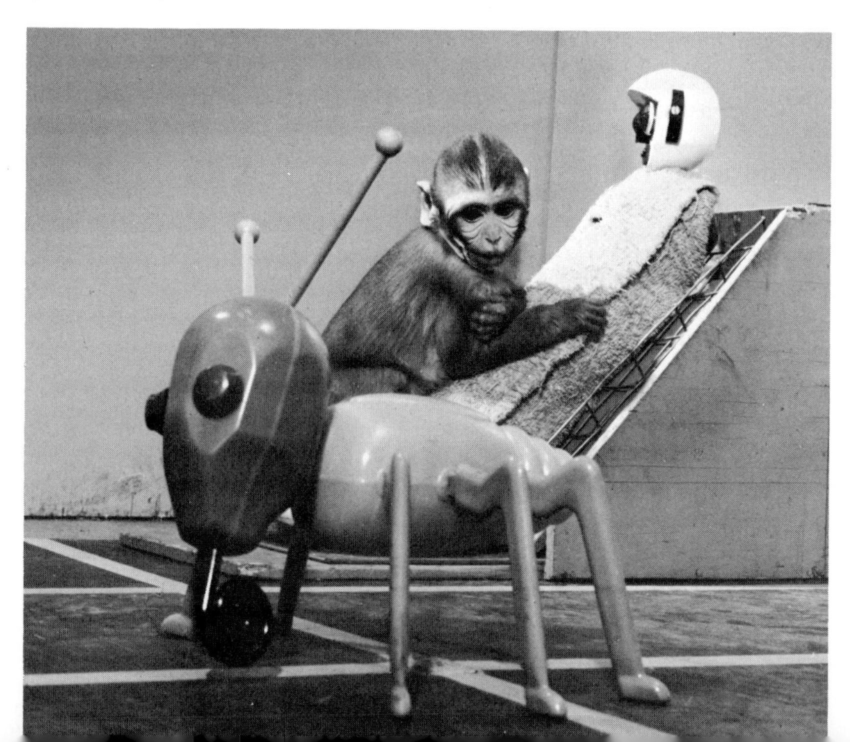

While some of the monkeys were being raised with surrogate mothers, a large number of infants were being reared in separate cages in a laboratory room. As these babies grew older, it became clear that their behavior was seriously abnormal. They sat for hours on end, simply staring off into space. Sometimes they would clasp their heads in their hands, rocking their bodies to and fro for minutes or hours at a time. Some of them developed compulsive habits, such as pinching one part of the body for long periods.

When normal monkeys are approached by a strange man, they are aggressive toward the interloper. Usually they jabber or scream at the stranger while making threatening gestures. Occasionally, they actually attack the stranger. The animals who were raised in isolation never attack an approaching man. Instead they attack themselves. They scratch, pinch, bite, or hit their own bodies. This behavior is also shown by disturbed human children.

The effects of the abnormal rearing are not confined to childhood. After these monkeys reach puberty, they have deep sexual problems. The males will start to approach females in the normal way. And the females will start to present their sex organs in the normal monkey fashion. But the animals are unable to carry the behavior beyond the initial steps. The males reared by themselves cannot even mate successfully with experienced females who take a vigorous part in the preliminaries.

Females who were raised alone have been mated with aggressive, sexually experienced males. Some of these females conceived and bore young. The mothers treated their babies with indifference at best, with outright abuse at worst. The infants persistently tried to nurse or to cling to their mothers, but they were always driven away. As these babies grew older, they showed extremely aggressive behavior toward other apes. In addition, they proved to be hypersexual, spending much more time in all sorts of sexual behavior than the normal monkeys. The deficiencies in the rearing of the mother were passed on, in a somewhat different form, to the offspring.

The results up to this point suggest that the relationship between mother and child is the most important factor in determining the pattern of adult behavior. This is not the whole story. One group of babies was left to be raised by their mothers, but isolated from all other monkeys. When tested later with others of the same age, the animals raised alone with their mothers were severely abnormal in their social and their sexual behavior.

A second group of infants were each raised with a terry cloth mother. For only twenty minutes a day, the babies were allowed together in a common room. At first, the babies spent the time exploring the room and each other. For the next three months, most of the time was spent in roughhouse play: wrestling, hair-pulling, and tag. The group of monkeys gradually worked out a complex pattern of violent activity, performed at blinding speed and involving all of the objects in the playroom, animate and inanimate. The social play was also increasingly interspersed with sexual play. These animals all developed social behavior which seemed reasonably normal for a monkey. They also could establish normal sexual relations and they mated successfully. This experiment suggests that play with other infants is even more important in the behavioral development of young monkeys than the relationship with the mother.

There seems to be a critical period in the social development of monkeys. If babies are isolated from others for the first 80 days of life and then allowed to mingle, they establish normal relations. If they are kept isolated for the first 180 days of life, they never develop appropriate social behavior.

Among the many interesting questions yet to be answered from the study of monkey behavior is whether some form of therapy can be worked out for animals who have been isolated, so they can be trained to acquire normal behavior relatively late in life.

GENETICS AND BEHAVIOR

In spite of the interest in the relation between genes and behavior, and the great advances in genetics made in the last decades, we still know little about the inheritance of behavior. Probably the clearest example of the effect of an altered genotype is the behavior of the yellow mutant of the fruit fly, *Drosophila.* The yellow gene is a sex-linked recessive which marks the carrier with a distinctive yellow body color. The yellow males are less successful in mating than normal males.

The mating behavior of the yellow males was analyzed in detail by Margaret Bastock. The first step in the normal mating behavior of *Drosophila melanogaster* is the approach of the male to the female. The male orients his body at right angles to the female and taps her on the abdomen. This behavior is called *orientation.* At this stage the female may move off, which interrupts the courtship sequence, or she may remain standing in the same spot. The male then raises the wing nearest the female and rapidly vibrates it: the behavior is called *vibration.* With each beat of the wings the male fly also emits a short pulse of sound. The organ producing this buzz has not been identified. Vibration plays an important part in courtship. Normal Drosophila males when placed with virgin females successfully mate 70 percent of the time. Males whose wings have been removed are successful only 32 percent of the time, presumably because they do not vibrate properly.

If the female still stands in position after the male has vibrated, he will lick her genitalia, jump on her back and will attempt to copulate. This final phase of the behavior is called *jumping*. The whole sequence —orientation, vibration, and jumping—goes along rapidly. There may be less than a minute between the bringing together of the male and the female and the beginning of copulation.

The behavior of the mutant yellow males had to be studied carefully in order to see the difference between their behavior and that of more successful normal males. The yellow males spend slightly less time vibrating, and slightly more time orienting. The differences are very slight: the normal male spends 22 percent of its time vibrating, the yellow male spends 18 percent of its time vibrating. There is one possibility in twenty that the difference in vibrating between the two groups comes by chance alone.

The difference in behavior is so slight that it is not easy to accept this as the cause of the greatly different success in mating. Another possibility is that females discriminate against yellow males because of their color. This is not so, since yellow males are also spurned when mating goes on in complete darkness. Therefore, the slight difference in vibration might be the determining factor. This conclusion is strengthened by the discovery that different species of *Drosophila* are kept from interbreeding by small differences in behavior (Chapter 10).

A good deal of work has been done on the behavioral genetics of rats, mice, and dogs. Their behavior is more interesting than that of fruit flies, but in every other way they are cumbersome animals for genetics. Different inbred strains have been compared for the ability to learn mazes, their aggressiveness, their preferences for alcohol, and so forth. The different strains are found to vary markedly in abilities and preferences.

Other experimenters have selectively bred animals which are particularly good, or particularly poor, at some type of behavior. By selection for several generations, strains of animals can be established which are better, or poorer, than the original stock in maze running, multiple choice problems, or other tasks. The strains always differ in a number of genetic loci, so the further genetic analysis is difficult. Behavioral genetics promises to be an interesting and growing field in the next years.

FURTHER READING

Bastock, M., "A Gene Mutation Which Changes a Behavior Pattern," *Evolution*, vol. 10 (1956), p. 421.

Caspari, E., "Refresher Course on Behavior Genetics: Synthesis and Outlook," *American Zoologist*, vol. 4 (1964), p. 169.

Ebert, J., *Interacting Systems in Development*, Modern Biology Series. New York: Holt, Rinehart and Winston, 1965.

Harlow, H. F., "Love in Infant Monkeys," *Scientific American* (June 1959), p. 68.

———, and M. K. Harlow, "Social Deprivation in Monkeys," *Scientific American* (November 1962), p. 136.

———, and ———, "Learning to Love," *American Scientist* (September 1966), p. 244.

Hess, E., "Imprinting in Animals," *Scientific American* (March 1958), p. 81.

Levine, R. P., *Genetics*, Modern Biology Series. New York: Holt, Rinehart and Winston, 1962.

McGill, T. E., ed., *Readings in Animal Behavior*, New York: Holt, Rinehart and Winston, 1965.

Sperry, R. W., "Mechanisms of Neural Maturation," Chapter 7 in *Handbook of Experimental Psychology*, S. S. Stevens, ed. New York: Wiley, 1951.

———, "The Eye and the Brain," *Scientific American* (May 1956), p. 48.

———, "The Growth of Nerve Circuits," *Scientific American* (November 1959), p. 68.

Thorpe, W. H., "The Language of Birds," *Scientific American* (October 1956), p. 128.

chapter 9

Social Behavior

Many animals live in groups or communities. These animals direct much of their behavior toward other members of the same species. The interaction of the individuals is the behavioral cement that keeps the group together and functioning. The groups range from loose, almost casual aggregations to enormously complex and interdependent units. To give an indication of the range of social behavior and how the individual's behavior fits it into the group, three different social groups will be discussed in this chapter.

HONEYBEES Insect societies have long fascinated biologists. The individual insect plays such a specialized role in the social order that the society has many of the

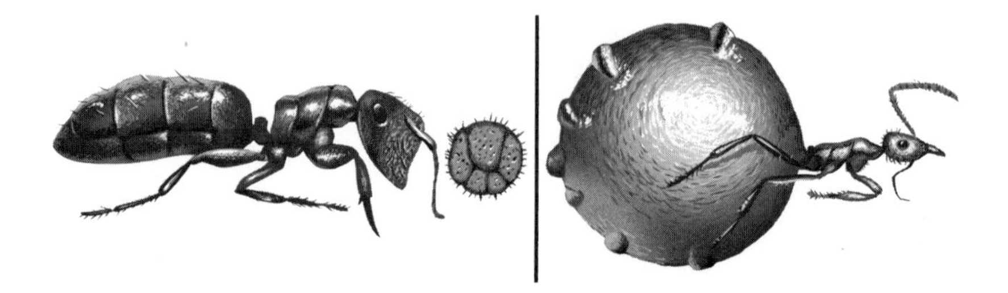

Fig. 9-1 *Two examples from ant colonies of members of castes whose bodies are highly modified to suit their special behavior. The ant on the left serves as a living door to the nest. The flat front of the head, shown head-on in the insert, is used to block the entrance. The ant on the right serves as a storage vessel for honey. (Dobzhansky,* Evolution, Genetics and Man, *Wiley, 1955.)*

attributes of a single, large superorganism. Ant societies probably show the most dramatic examples of specialization. Some species have soldiers whose heads are modified to serve as a door, closing the entrance of the nest (Figure 9-1). When approached by an ant from the nest, the gatekeeper backs away and opens the tunnel entrance. Other ant societies have individuals who become living barrels to store honey in the nest (Figure 9-1).

The honeybee society is somewhat less specialized; consequently, bees are easier to study and a good deal of experimental work has been completed. The basis of the honeybee social order is an extreme reproductive specialization. The reproductively competent females—the queens—mate only a few times during their lives. The sperm is stored in a reservoir in the female's reproductive tract. An unfertilized egg develops into a male bee. Usually unfertilized eggs are laid in the spring. Fertilized eggs develop into females; most of the eggs laid by the female are fertilized. The newly hatched female larva may develop into either a worker or a queen, depending on her diet. The diet of the future queens includes a substance, royal jelly, secreted by the salivary glands of worker bees. The other female larvae develop into workers; they are not able to reproduce under normal circumstances.

The ovaries of workers will begin to develop if the queen is removed from the hive. When the queen is present, she secretes a "queen substance," which turns out to be a rather simple organic acid, 9-oxo-2-decenoic acid. The formula is as follows:

$$CH_3-\underset{\underset{O}{\|}}{C}-CH_2-CH_2-CH_2-CH_2-CH_2-CH{=}CH-COOH$$

The queen substance is licked by the workers tending the queen. One of the basic characteristics of the honeybee society is that the individual members are constantly exchanging food (Figure 9-2). In one experiment, six foragers from a colony of 25,000 were allowed to drink some sugar water containing radioactive phosphorus. Two hours later, 29 percent of the bees in the colony were radioactive, 24 hours later, 60 percent of the bees were labeled. The exchange spreads not only food, but also queen substance throughout the hive. The queen substance has two actions. It inhibits the development of the worker's ovaries. It also inhibits the behavior of queen rearing, so larvae are not fed royal jelly. The queen substance is an example of a social hormone, or pheromone.

The worker bees take on a variety of tasks. One important question in the social order is how the efforts of the workers are allocated so that all of the business of the hive is done. Early evidence suggested

Fig. 9-2 *A group of bees on the honey comb. One worker is begging a drop of food from another. Social hormones are rapidly distributed throughout the hive along with the exchanged food. (Syd Greenberg, Photo Researchers.)*

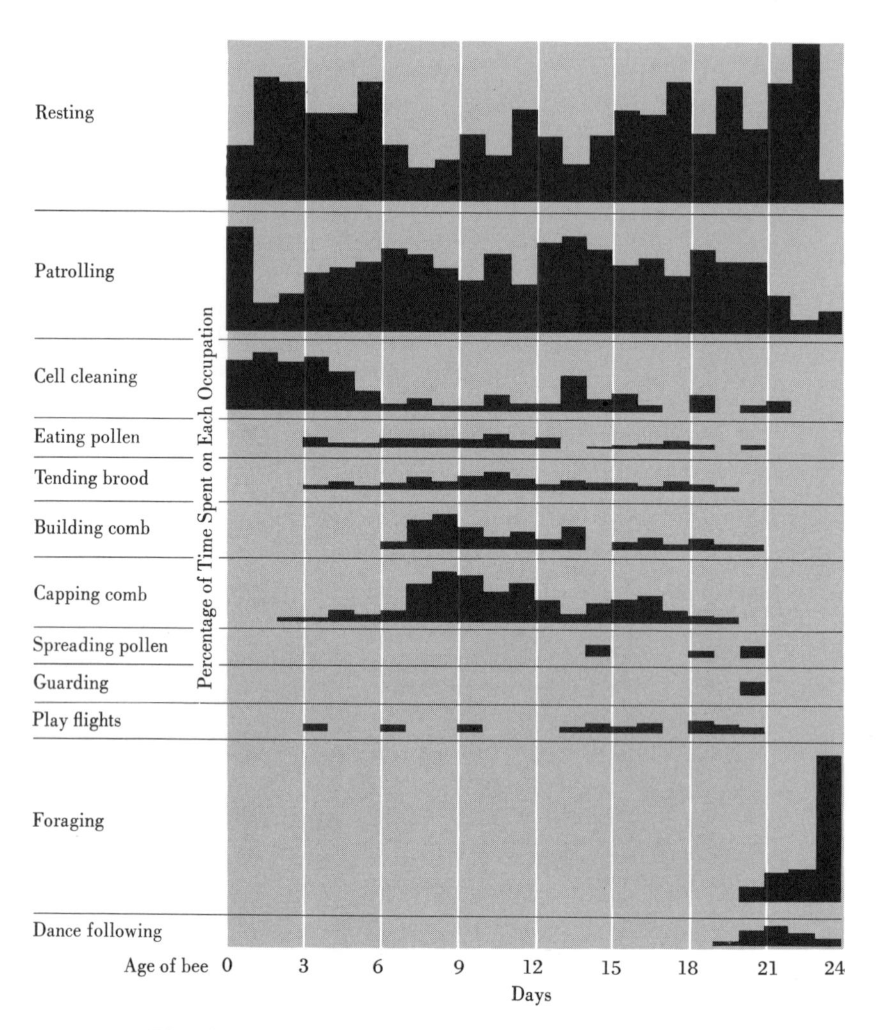

Fig. 9-3 *The distribution of effort by an individual worker bee which is followed for many hours during her life. Notice particularly the amount of time spent patrolling and resting. (Reprinted by permission of the publishers from Martin Lindauer,* Communication Among Social Bees, *Cambridge, Mass.: Harvard University Press, Copyright 1961, by the President and Fellows of Harvard College.)*

that the task depended solely on the age of the worker. It was believed that newly emerged workers started as hive cleaners and graduated to more complex tasks as they matured. After three days, the workers took up nursing, which involved feeding and tending the larvae. On about the tenth day of adult life, the worker became a builder, spending the greater part of the day secreting wax from special glands and building the hexagonal cells that make up the honeycomb. On the seventeenth day, the worker began to meet incoming foragers, relieving them of their load of nectar and pollen and distributing food throughout the hive. The worker on the twentieth day took station as a guard at the entrance of the hive. (The guards recognize homecoming bees by their scent. In good seasons, when there is abundant nectar, incoming bees are allowed into the hive after a brief inspection. But if food is in short supply, bees from other colonies are repulsed at the hive entrance, and interlopers are killed.) On about the twenty-first day the worker bee finally became a forager, flying out for nectar and pollen. This sequence of activities shows the many types of specialized behavior a worker bee can perform.

Lindauer studied the sequence of tasks by marking individual worker bees when they first emerged as adults, and then keeping constant watch on their activities. The division of the time of one worker bee for the first twenty-four days of life is shown in Figure 9-3. The first surprising point is that the bee spends a great deal of time resting, despite the proverbial busyness. Out of 177 hours of observation, this worker spent 69 hours and 53 minutes doing nothing whatsoever.

Lindauer found that much time is spent patrolling, simply walking through the hive. Patrolling is important in regulating the work of the hive. Whenever the worker finishes one job, she is likely to patrol the hive until she encounters a job that needs doing. The division of labor is not achieved by each animal going through a rigid, inflexible sequence. On the seventeenth day, for example, the worker cleaned cells, built honeycomb, guarded the hive entrance, went on play flights, foraged, and followed dancers. The worker is able to take up whatever tasks present themselves, though not equally ready for all tasks at each age.

TEMPERATURE REGULATION

The temperature within a bee hive is closely regulated; it usually varies only from 34.5 to 35.5°C. If it is cold outside, and the temperature in the hive falls below 34.5°C., the workers sit on the comb and move their wings up and down. The muscular work produces heat to warm the hive.

If the temperature climbs above 35.5°C., the first behavior elicited is fanning. A group of workers go to the hive entrance and use their wings to propel a current of air into the hive. If the outside air is cool, fanning will lower the temperature in the hive. If the outside temperature is above 34°C., the hive is cooled by the evaporating water. Foragers, who bring water to the hive, are met by other workers, who take the water into the comb and sprinkle it on the cells containing the brood. Other workers spread the drops into a film which evaporates and cools the hive.

This is an example of community behavior which depends on the coordinated activity of many individuals. On a hot day in midsummer, most of the bees in the hive will be working at cooling. The group behavior develops in this way. The first response to an increase in the temperature of the hive is by the nurses. They spread their store of honey over the brood cells to evaporate. They then beg more honey water from nearby bees, who surrender their store and in turn beg from a neighbor. A wave of begging moves through the hive, and the total supply of honey water in the hive is moved to the brood cells. The workers who greet returning foragers avidly beg from those bringing in the poorest food, that is, the most dilute sugar solution. A forager bringing in good food will be hard put to find a worker to relieve her of her load; a forager who brings in watery nectar will be met by three or four begging workers. The intensity of the begging behavior stimulates the foragers to bring in dilute nectar, or even to switch over and begin to collect water. When the hive has been cooled sufficiently, foragers returning with watery nectar are ignored, while those returning with rich food are greeted by several workers.

SWARMING When the population of a hive grows too large, there is not enough queen substance to prevent the development of a second queen. The old queen and a band of workers will then leave the parent hive and set out to find a new site to build a new home. The swarming bees assemble as a cluster near the hive. A few scouts leave the cluster and fly out to survey the surrounding area. The returning scouts perform the tail-wagging dance, which here indicates the direction and distance of a possible site. The dances recruit other scouts, who fly out to the proposed locations. At first the dancers will point to many possibilities. After days or even weeks, the choices are narrowed down. More and more of the scouts point toward one favored site. When a consensus is reached, the whole swarm moves to the site and begins to construct a new nest.

The honeybee society has been pictured as rigid and monolithic by biologists overwhelmed by the extreme reproductive specialization. A closer look shows that the daily operations of the hive depend on the versatility of the workers, and their behavior in undertaking the needed job at the proper time. None of the details of the selection of tasks or the interaction of individual bees with one another are known. A worker's life is full of occasions in which two bees meet to exchange food and tactile stimuli. Perhaps these meetings reinforce certain kinds of behavior and these social reinforcers may be important for integrating the society.

HERRING GULLS Behavioral science has always profited from the observations of naturalists, who will undergo the bleakest discomforts to painstakingly watch the behavior of some favorite animal. The skilled naturalist becomes so familiar with the subjects that he can detect the slightest nuance in their behavior. The naturalist of today rigorously avoids the temptation to endow the animals with human emotions and feelings, and they often supplement observation with experiment. An outstanding example is the study by Tinbergen of the herring gulls of the North Sea.

The gulls studied by Tinbergen live on the sand dunes along the coast of Holland. All of the breeding and the raising of the young goes on in special grounds occupied only in the spring and summer. In early March, the gulls begin to fly in vast groups over the breeding grounds. Not one lands. For fifteen minutes, the entire group soars and circles overhead, then flies away in formation. When the weather is fair, the visit is repeated daily. With each visit, the flock flies slightly lower. Finally, one day late in March, a single gull lands, stops for a moment or two on the top of a dune, elongates its neck and stares in all directions. Then it rejoins the flock and all fly off together. One day, in early April, the whole flock lands at once and takes possession of the breeding ground.

Most of the birds in the flock were probably reared on this breeding ground, and the adult birds raised young here the year before. After the breeding season, the male and female are thought to go their own way for the winter months. Usually, the pair find one another again in the period just before the flock reoccupies the breeding ground. Herring gulls are usually strictly monogamous.

Each pair tries to occupy the same spot on the dunes where they were the year before. The pair will defend a territory 2 to 50 yards in diameter against other gulls. If another gull crosses the boundary of the territory, the male walks toward the interloper using a peculiar, rigid stride. The wings may be lifted slightly, so they stand out from the body. Tinbergen calls this the "upright threat posture." The threat usually immediately impresses the intruder, who begins to move away. The defender will then charge toward the other gull. The charge hastens the intruder's flight, and soon the territory is free of trespassers.

Sometimes the male and the female move together to defend the territory, particularly if the intruders are also a pair. They rush toward the intruders, stop, point their heads downward, bend the legs, and start rhythmic pecking movements. The pecks always stop short of the ground. At the same time, they call "houh-houh-houh-houh." They may make scratching movements with the legs. The intruding pair often respond with the same performance. The incident will end with the retreat of the trespassers or with a fight between the males. Both males take up the threat position about a foot apart. Suddenly, one of the birds tears a slip of vegetation from the ground, waves it in the bill for a moment, and then tosses it aside. The other bird may also tear up a piece of grass, and the two animals alternate between the threat posture and grass pulling for several minutes. Suddenly, one bird rushes at the other, pecking and attempting to seize hold of the adversary's body. The two hit freely at one another with their powerful wings. The loser may receive a serious drubbing.

Many of the birds on the breeding grounds are youngsters who have not yet paired. These birds settle in dense groups or "clubs," in spots between the dunes where there is a cover of green vegetation. The birds in the clubs spend much of their time dozing or preening. Occasionally a female walks toward a male. Her neck is pulled in and her head is horizontal, pointing forward. Now and again she tosses her head, uttering a melodic "klio" each time. She walks around the male several times. Sometimes the male reacts by stretching upward to his full height. If another male is nearby, the male who is propositioned will drive off the other with threats or even by fighting. At other times the male will stretch his neck forward, calling "mew." The male and female walk together for a few yards, stop, and then make some of the movements normally used in nest building. At other times the propositioned male will begin to twist and to turn his neck. In response, the female speeds up her neck tossing. She struts back and forth before the male. Every now and then she seizes his bill in her own. After a while the male regurgitates some half-digested food, which the female avidly pecks from his mouth.

The males and females go through these ceremonies time after time. At first the females will make advances toward a number of males, but gradually a pair of birds spends more and more time with one another. Finally they leave the club as a pair. After the pair is formed, the female will start to proposition the male as before. But now the male never regurgitates food; instead, he begs for food with tossing movements of his head. After a while the male moves behind the female, with his head stretched out and still tossing. The male then starts to give a rhythmic harsh cry. He jumps on the female's back and they copulate.

The new pair work together to build a nest. Both collect straw and moss and help to shape it. After the first egg is laid, either the male or the female is always at the nest incubating the eggs. If an egg rolls out of the nest, the parent retrieves it (see Chapter 5, Ethology and Releasers).

The incubating birds show strong defensive behavior. If a dog or a human starts to walk into the breeding grounds, the gulls begin to call "hahaha." The call alerts nearby birds and they take up a hue and cry. Some of the gulls may charge the intruder by swooping down at high speed again and again. However, they rarely strike, pulling away just before contact is made.

The chicks hatch from the eggs in June. During the rest of the summer they stay in and around the nest. They are fed by the parents and are sufficiently grown to leave with the group at the end of summer.

At first it seems surprising that such large numbers of birds congregate and then do so little together. The paired birds interact mainly by defending territorial boundaries and sharing the burden of feeding the young. The only activity that involves the cooperation of many birds is the defense against large predators. This must be one of the primary advantages leading to the evolution of the behavior on the breeding grounds. Tinbergen believes that the territorial behavior is advantageous in reducing predation of the eggs. The eggs and the nests are quite well camouflaged. Since they are spread out widely, they are not easy to find.

CHIMPANZEE SOCIETY

Chimpanzees are one of science's favorite animals. They are used in laboratories around the world; they have been raised side by side with human babies; they have been rocketed into space. The unfortunate fact is that we know surprisingly little about their behavior in their natural habitat. Only a handful of sturdy naturalists have attempted to observe free-living chimpanzees. The problems are indeed difficult. Chimpanzees usually live in the dense rain forests. They move through the trees rapidly to avoid natural enemies and unwelcome intruders.

One investigator studied the behavior of chimpanzees which left the shelter of the forest to feast on bananas and paw-paws grown on a plantation. He hid on a platform 80 feet up in a solitary tree. He had to reach the blind before the chimpanzees were about in the morning and he always had to remain until they had left for the night. On windy days the tree swayed so badly that it was impossible to use field glasses. An expert field worker who followed chimpanzees into the forest, watching them from afar with powerful binoculars, averaged one and one half hours of observation per day. It takes dedication to study chimpanzees. Perhaps the most successful method is to habituate the animals to the observer's presence. When Jane Goodall began to study the chimpanzees in Tanganyika, they ran each time she came within 500 yards. After eight months of almost daily effort, she could approach to 100 feet without disrupting their activities (Figure 9-4).

Fig. 9-4 *A family group of chimpanzees in the Gombe stream game reserve of Tanganyika. The daughter, Fifi* (left), *nuzzles her baby brother, who is held in the mother's arm. Fifi was possessive of her brother and would not allow other young chimpanzees to come near him. (Baron Hugo van Lawick © National Geographic Society.)*

Fig. 9-5 *A mature male chimpanzee asleep on a day nest. (Baron Hugo van Lawick © National Geographic Society.)*

Fig. 9-6 *Fifi using a stripped-down blade of grass as a tool for collecting insects. (© National Geographic Society.)*

The chimpanzees in the forest spend most of the daylight hours in the trees. At night each adult animal usually makes a nest by bending and interlacing branches. Construction takes only one to five minutes. During the rainy season, nests will also be made for a rest during the day (Figure 9-5).

The major foods are fruits, leaf buds, ants, and termites. The chimpanzee collects insects by selecting a short stick and thrusting the stick into the nest. After a few moments, the stick is pulled out, swarming with insects to be licked off (Figure 9-6). A famous series of experiments in behavior showed that chimpanzees will use a stick to reach for a suspended banana, or even join two sticks together to reach for food beyond the range of one stick. This behavior was regarded as a sign of the sudden solution by the animal of a problem found only in the laboratory. We had to wait almost thirty years to learn that chimpanzees in nature use sticks for collecting food every day. Occasionally, chimpanzees hunt, kill, and eat small monkeys or bushpigs. Sometimes human babies have been captured and eaten.

The chimpanzees usually travel in bands. But the composition of the bands changes frequently and animals move freely from one type of band to another. Some bands have adults only; there are no adolescents or mothers with children. The adult bands travel long distances through the forest. Another type of band has only adult males. Others have only mothers and their young. Probably the most common group is the mixed band, which is made up of both sexes and all age groups. The bands have a prominent effect on the behavior of the individuals. When a chimpanzee is alone, it moves slowly and with sober dignity. As soon as it joins a group, all of its movements are speeded up, and the chimpanzee gives the impression of eagerness and alertness.

The leadership of the bands seems to be almost as flexible as their composition. Sometimes a group of graying adult males travels in the van of a large band. On occasion, one of the old males drops out of the band and remains behind. He watches carefully for a while and then hurries to rejoin the group. These are the only indications of leadership in chimpanzee bands, in which the relations are informal and reciprocal. The loose organization of chimpanzee society may reflect the absence of natural enemies in the regions where the studies were undertaken. There is no animal preying on the chimpanzee and, therefore, little need for defensive behavior.

The casual chimpanzee groups are quite different from other primate societies. A band of baboons, for example, is organized around one dominant male. He takes strict precedence in sexual relations with receptive females, is the leader when the group is threatened or attacked, and is closely followed by the mothers with infants.

There is no dominant male in the chimpanzee society. A female will mate with a number of different males; the males show no sign of jealousy or possessiveness. Sometimes mating is initiated by the male, who displays himself by swinging from branch to branch with the hair on his head, shoulders, and arms erected for almost one minute. If the female is receptive, she will go into a crouch almost immediately. At other times, the female solicits copulation by crouching before the male.

Newborn chimpanzees spend most of their first months clinging to the mother. The infants must cling firmly as the mother swings rapidly from tree to tree. The clinging to a soft object, which is a prominent part of the behavior of the young in the laboratory, is a matter of life or death in the wild.

The major activity of children and adolescents is playing. They live in a group, so most of their play is with other youngsters. This is just the sort of experience laboratory tests have shown to be essential for the normal behavior development of monkeys (see Chapter 8, Development of Monkey Behavior). A common game is mock-fighting, in which babies wrestle and chase one another. Sometimes they play at nest building. As they grow older, there is an increasing attention to sexual and maternal play. As with other animals, the play of the young consists primarily of practicing adult occupations.

Fig. 9-7 *Two males greeting one another. The chimp in the foreground is touching the other's scrotum with his left hand. This is frequently part of the greeting ceremony. (© The National Geographic Society.)*

Displays of temper between adult chimpanzees are common. Now and then there is a fight, but usually it lasts only a few seconds and little damage is done. When one chimpanzee is angry, the others will often greet him with an "appeasement grin." The lower lip is drawn down to expose the teeth and gums. The appeaser will often reach out to touch the lips or the scrotum of an angry animal. Females will sometimes appease by turning around and presenting their sex organs. The appeasement ceremonies usually calm the angry chimpanzee and restore peace to the group.

Mutual grooming is one of the most important positive interactions among the chimpanzees in a group. Males are most likely to groom with other males, and females with females, so the activity is not sexual. Sometimes two animals come together, sit down, and immediately begin grooming. At other times, one animal solicits grooming by approaching another and standing nearby with head bowed. A pair may spend hours at a time lazily grooming one another, sitting with half-closed eyes, slowly smacking their lips.

Greeting is another important social ceremony. The common, everyday greeting is for the animals to touch each other's bodies with the flat or the back of the hand. If the two animals have been separated for a longer time, they approach one another with soft, panting grunts. They then throw their arms around one another and embrace (Figure 9-7). While performing this greeting, males usually have an erection of the penis, even though there is no reason to think that the behavior has sexual connotations.

The most remarkable—and least understood—chimpanzee social occasion is the carnival. Some animals in the depth of the forest begin to drum rhythmically on tree trunks and to hoot and scream. They create a tremendous uproar. Other chimpanzees may travel through the forest to join the group, so that the volume of the sound increases even more. The noise becomes so loud that even experienced listeners may be apprehensive. The carnival may continue for hours. No one has ever observed a carnival and no one is sure what the animals do. Possibly the carnival includes dancing. Captive chimpanzees often form a circle and dance around a tree or post, stepping lightly with one foot and heavily with the other, keeping time with one another. They wag their heads in time to the dance and individual animals perform solo variations. A familiar human will be drawn into the circle of dancers. In fact, the human can often start a dance by beginning to move about the circle, rhythmically stomping his feet.

REVIEWING THREE ANIMAL SOCIETIES

The brief resumé of the broad characteristics of three animal societies emphasizes the variety of the groups and the different functions societies can serve. The basis of social life is the interaction of individual members, who exchange food, water, body care, and sexual favors. These exchanges must often reinforce behavior which binds the group together. Insect societies are based on large numbers of individuals with a short life span. The insects live in a tightly organized, specialized body. Chimpanzee societies, at the other extreme, appear to be relatively loosely organized. The young develop slowly and the only really stable social grouping is for the rearing of the juvenile animals. Experiments have shown that the young chimpanzee cannot develop properly away from the social group, any more than a honeybee can live by itself. In both cases the social group is an obligatory part of the normal life history.

THE REGULATION OF POPULATION SIZE

What sets the upper limit to the number of animals making up a population? The classic answer is that the number of individuals increases at an accelerating rate until the available food or space are used up. When this boundary is reached, the numbers are thinned by famine or disease. Or perhaps the numbers are kept below the disaster level by predators.

However, the mammalian populations that have been carefully studied do not seem to obey the classic rules. When mice are reared in the laboratory in a large cage with abundant food, the population size levels off and remains relatively constant with numbers far below those needed to take up all of the standing room. Field studies show that the same regulation of population size occurs in groups of mammals in nature. Several changes in the animals account for the result. When the population density rises, young animals are delayed in attaining sexual maturity, so mating begins at a later age. The sexual cycle of mature females takes longer, so they ovulate less frequently. There is a rise in the number of fetuses that die in the uterus. All of these changes act to lower the birth rate. There is also an increase in the death rate among new born and nursing animals, partly owing to deficiencies in maternal care. Fewer animals reach sexual maturity.

The effects of high population density on the birth rate and on infant mortality are well established, but the mechanisms underlying the changes are still being unravelled. In dense populations there is an increase in aggressive behavior. The aggressive bouts usually involve more threat than actual combat. However, they produce measurable endocrine changes, especially in the participant who retreats before a more dominant or aggressive neighbor. The adrenals increase markedly in weight. The amounts of hormones released from the adrenal cortex are raised. The abnormally high hormone titers may account for at least some of the reproductive malfunctions.

In several species of mouse, if a newly fertilized female is placed with a strange male, there is a good chance that her pregnancy will fail. If the male is from an entirely different strain, then there is an excellent chance that she will not produce young. The effect of the strange male can be prevented by cutting the female's olfactory nerve before they are brought together. Or the effect of the male can be duplicated by exposing the female to a ball of cotton which the male has lived with. Smell is the stimulus for the end of the pregnancy; however, we do not understand the other steps in the response.

Some biologists believe that human populations are also regulated by unknown factors brought into play by crowding. The birth rate has fallen in parts of the world, such as Scandinavia, where high population density is the rule. The regulation of population size has a vital role in human welfare—this is one of the aspects of behavioral science in which an increase in research effort is imperative.

FURTHER READING

Christian, J. J., and D. E. Davis, "Endocrines, Behavior, and Populations," *Science*, vol. 146 (1964), p. 1550.

Davis, D. E., *Integral Animal Behavior*. New York: Macmillan, 1966.

DeVore, I., ed., *Primate Behavior*. New York: Holt, Rinehart and Winston, 1965.

———, and S. L. Washburn, "The Social Life of Baboons," *Scientific American* (June 1961), p. 62.

Kortlandt, A., "Chimpanzees in the Wild," *Scientific American* (May 1962), p. 128.

Lindauer, M., *Communication among Social Bees*. Cambridge, Mass.: Harvard University Press, 1961.

Portmann, A., *Animals as Social Beings*. New York: Viking, 1961.

Ribbands, R., *Behavior and Social Life of Honeybees*. New York: Dover, 1953.

Tinbergen, N., "The Evolution of Behavior in Gulls," *Scientific American* (December 1960), p. 118.

———, *Herring Gull's World*. New York: Basic Books, 1961.

chapter **10**

Evolution and Behavior

There is a two-sided relation between evolution and behavior. Like other animal characters, behavior varies from animal to animal within a population, it is exposed to natural selection and, hence, to evolution. The evolution of behavior was perfectly clear to Charles Darwin, who wrote an important treatise, *The Expression of the Emotions in Man and in Animals.* The other side is that changes in behavior often play an important role in the origin of new species.

BEHAVIOR AND THE ORIGIN OF SPECIES

New animal species are generally thought to arise in the following way. An existing species is subdivided into two separate populations.

The separation is usually produced by a geographical barrier which prevents the ready intermingling of the two groups. The barrier may be a sea, a river, a desert, a mountain range, or other obstacle. Thus, geography prevents interbreeding between the two populations. As time passes, the two populations are selected for slightly different characteristics because of slight differences in the environment, so the genetic makeup of the two populations becomes dissimilar. If the two populations are small, genetic differences can also arise by a chance process called genetic drift. Now suppose that the geographical barrier between the two populations disappears, or by some other means the two populations once again come in contact with one another. If the two populations can interbreed successfully, they will lose any distinctive characters and will merge into one large group. However, if interbreeding does not take place, or if it occurs infrequently, the two populations will live side by side while remaining distinct. They are reproductively isolated and regarded as two distinct species.

Reproductive isolation can occur in different ways. For instance, animals from the two populations may mate but the hybrids then fail to develop properly. One of the most common mechanisms is that the behavior of the two groups has become somewhat different, so the courtship or copulation behavior no longer dovetails.

In Chapter 8, the courtship behavior of the fruit fly, *Drosophila melanogaster* was described, along with some experiments on the genetics of behavior. Different species of *Drosophila* have also been studied to see whether there are differences in mating behavior. This is a difficult task because the courtship movements are performed very rapidly and the entire sequence may last less than a minute. Some investigators watch the two flies while listening to the ticking of a metronome. Each time the metronome ticks, the investigator marks down a shorthand symbol to show what the male fly is doing at that instant. The metronome is usually set to give forty-four beats per minute.

The courtship movements of the different species of *Drosophila* studied so far are quite similar (see Chapter 8, Genetics and Behavior). The male begins by orienting at right angles to the female, tapping on her abdomen with his front legs. He then curls his abdomen underneath himself, extends the wing closest to the female's head and vibrates it rapidly. He next jumps onto the female's back, attempting to make contact with her genitalia. If contact is made, copulation proceeds.

The male's courtship continues on its course without any special signal from the female. If courtship is going well, the female simply stands in one spot. Sometimes the female walks away from the male. He follows and continues courting, but with a noticable loss of intensity. If the female has been fertilized already, she extrudes her genitalia at the male. This gesture inhibits further courtship.

The mating behavior of eleven species of *Drosophila* found in North America has been carefully studied. The movements of courtship are similar from species to species, but interbreeding rarely occurs. The behavioral differences causing reproductive isolation are remarkably subtle. For instance, *D. pseudoobscura* and *D. persimilis* live side by side in the western United States, but fewer than one in 1000 of the flies captured in nature are hybrids. So far the only difference detected in the courtship of the males is in the frequency of the sound pulse given during the vibration movement. The sound during the pulse given by *persimilis* males is at about 480 Hz; *pseudoobscura* males buzz at 290 Hz. Though conclusive experimental proof is lacking, this may be the behavioral basis of the reproductive isolation.

EVOLUTION OF BEHAVIOR

One of the nicest examples of the evolution of behavior comes from comparing different species belonging to a group known as the empid or "dance flies." In one species, *Empis scutellata*, the male fly prepares for mating by capturing a small insect. He carries the captive into a swarm of female dance flies, and presents the prey to one of the females. Presentation is accompanied by an intricate dance. The pair settle into the shrubbery where they copulate. During copulation, the female generally feeds on the gift.

The behavior of *Hilara quadrivittata* is almost the same, except that the male loosely binds the captive in a net of silk before presenting it to the female. In other species, the silk case becomes more elaborate. *E. poplitea* male spin a balloon of silk about the prey. Then, the wrapping becomes more important than the gift. The male of *H. thoracica* spins an intricate case of silk about the prey. But the case is not too efficient in holding the captive insect, who often falls free before the case is presented to the female, but mating proceeds nonetheless. In *H. maura*, the male will often substitute a small slip of vegetation, such as the petal of a flower, for the insect. Either flower petal or prey is enmeshed in a silken case and is offered to the female as a prerequisite for mating. The final species is *H. sartor.* The male spins a compact silken case while in flight. The case is presented to the female in the usual fashion, but it never contains food.

This is a clear example of how the evolution of a behavior pattern can be understood by the comparative study of a group of closely related species. It shows how certain types of behavior can be understood only by knowing their evolution. The presentation of an empty silken case to a female as a prelude to mating makes little sense. When the evolution of the behavior is studied, the nature of the ceremony becomes obvious.

EVOLUTION OF BEE DANCING

Some behavior is so extraordinary and so specialized that it is difficult to imagine how it ever originated. How did honeybees ever evolve the dances they use for communication? The first step in the study of the evolution of dancing behavior was to determine whether there is variation among the different races of honeybees that are geographically separated and have little chance to interbreed. It soon becomes apparent that there are differences; von Frisch likes to call them dialects in the bee's language. For example, Italian bees have a dance slower than the Austrian bees from the other side of the Alps. Mixed hives can be formed experimentally, containing both Italian and Austrian bees. When an Italian forager returns to the hive from a food source 100 meters away, she dances the wagging dance to indicate direction and distance. Austrian bees are given the correct direction by the dance, but they interpret the distance differently; they will fly out to a point 120 meters from the hive.

Another step in trying to understand the evolution of honeybee behavior is to study closely related species. Lindauer found that the dwarf honeybee (*Apis florea*) dances to indicate direction and distance of the food, but the dance is always done out of doors when the sun is

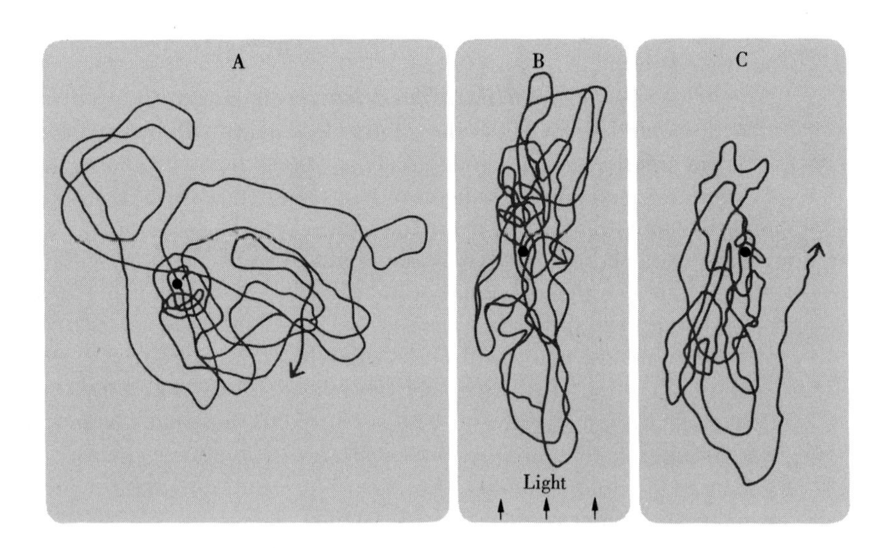

Fig. 10-1 *(A) The pattern of movements on a horizontal surface of a fly who had been stimulated for a movement with a drop of sugar water. (B) The pattern performed by stimulated fly on a horizontal surface when a beam of light comes from one side. The movements performed in darkness on a vertical surface. (Adapted from V. G. Dethier, "Communication by Insects: Physiology of Dancing,"* Science, *vol. 125, 22 February 1957, pp. 331–336.)*

shining. They dance on a special horizontal platform built on top of the honeycomb. They never dance on a vertical surface. Apparently they have never evolved the ability to translate the dance from a horizontal to a vertical surface.

A different form of communication is used by stingless bees of the genus *Trigona*. The first experiments showed that once a rich food source, placed within range of their hive, is discovered by the scouts, large numbers of bees come out to carry in food. The stingless bees are as effective as the honeybee in alerting the hive to a new food source. However, when stingless bee scouts return to the hive, they do not perform anything like a round dance or a wagging dance. They run about excitedly, making a peculiar humming noise. The running and the sound seem to alert the other bees to the discovery of the food, but give no indication of either direction or distance. The alerted bees, nevertheless, leave the hive and go to the food. The question of their ability to locate a food source was not easily resolved.

The first clue came from watching the scouts on the flight back. They would land every two or three yards and spend a moment on a twig or blade of grass. They seemed to be marking the path by laying down an odor trail. After alerting the other bees in the hive, the scout would fly out to the food source once again. It seemed likely that the bees were guided to the food by following the scout and the odor trail. Lindauer tested this idea by placing a hive on one side of a lake, and a feeding station on the opposite side. Scout bees discovered the food and flew back to the hive across the lake. They could not lay an odor trail on the water. The scouts would return to the food, but they never brought along other foragers. Then a rope was strung across the lake. Now the returning scouts laid an odor trail on the rope and soon large numbers of bees followed the scouts back across the rope to the food source. Social bees have evolved at least two distinct methods for directing others to a good food source.

An unexpected clue to the evolution of the bee dance was discovered by Dethier. He was studying the feeding behavior of flies. When a fly walks across a horizontal surface and encounters a drop of sugar water, it stops to drink. Then the fly begins to walk in a distinctive circular path, which is an effective search pattern to run into other drops of sugar water which might be in the area (Figure 10-1). If a light is shining from one side, then the pattern is no longer circular, but is shaped like an ellipse, with the long axis toward the light. If the fly is on a vertical surface in darkness, then the path is oriented to the pull of gravity.

It is not too farfetched to imagine that some primitive form of search behavior like that shown by the fly could be the starting point for the evolution of the bee dance.

BEHAVIOR AND THE EVOLUTION OF STRUCTURE

During the voyage of the *Beagle*, Charles Darwin made a memorable stop at the Galapagos Islands. This group of islands in the Pacific lies on the equator, 600 miles west of the coast of Equador. The islands were formed by volcanos that grew up from the bottom of the sea. All of the animals and plants populating the islands are descended from ancestors who drifted, flew, were carried or blown from other shores. Most of the ancestors probably came from South America, but one mollusk is clearly descended from a species found in Polynesia, several thousand miles to the west.

The islands are now inhabited by fourteen species of the finch—Darwin's finches. They all probably evolved from a common ancestor who flew in from Central or South America. When the finches began to populate the Galapagos Islands, probably there were few other land birds to compete for the different types of food available. The finches populated the different islands in the group. The bands in the different islands were geographically isolated from one another, satisfying the precondition for the formation of new species. Some of the finch species are seed eaters, as their ancestors were. They have all of the behavior appropriate to birds feeding on seeds, and they also have heavy beaks for cracking tough seeds. Another species makes the nectar from the flowers of the prickly pear an important part of its diet. Like other nectar-feeding birds, this finch has evolved a beak with a slight curve and a split tongue. Another species has a stout, straight beak; it searches the bark of trees for insects (Figure 10-2).

These finches have evolved both the behavior and the anatomy to exploit a food source. There is one species that has evolved specialized behavior to make up for an anatomical deficit. This finch feeds in the same manner as a woodpecker. Like woodpeckers everywhere, this species has evolved the specialized ability to walk up and down vertical tree trunks. When a conventional woodpecker has dug a hole in a tree, which reaches down to an insect, it inserts its functionally long tongue into the hole to remove the prey. The finch has not evolved a specialized tongue. The need has been met by the evolution of special behavior. When the hole is dug in the tree, the finch picks up a cactus spine an inch or two long. The spine is held lengthwise in the beak, and is poked down the hole until the insect starts to crawl out (Figure 10-2). As the insect emerges, the finch drops the spine and grabs the food. A highly effective behavior substitutes for a special structure.

The literature of natural history is filled with other examples of the side-by-side evolution of structure and of function. Sometimes part of the animal's body is used in an important display. For example, recall the behavior of the male three-spined stickleback. During fights at the edge of his territory, he displays his red belly to other males.

Fig. 10-2 *At the top are three species of Darwin's finch from the Galapagos Islands. The bird on the left eats seeds, which it crushes in its heavy beak. The one in the middle feeds on the pulp of the prickly pear, which it probes for with its long beak. The species on the right searches for insects in the twigs and vegetation covering the ground. Notice how well the beak shape is correlated with feeding habits. Below is a species of finch that extracts insects from holes in tree trunks. It probes for the prey with a cactus spine or a small twig selected for the purpose. (Adapted from D. Lack,* Darwin's Finches, *Cambridge University Press.)*

When courting the female, the display of the red belly is again a prominent part of the male's behavior. Model experiments show that the response of the other animal depends upon the red color, while many other aspects of the male's normal appearance are dispensable.

Almost the same statements can be made about the breast of the robin. The male European robin displays its red breast during conflicts at the edge of its territory and also to the female during courtship. A male will attack a bundle of red feathers placed in its territory and totally ignore a real stuffed young robin which lacks the red breast (Figure 10-3). Again the evolution of behavior and of a striking coloration have gone hand in hand. Hundreds of similar examples could be cited.

TRENDS IN BEHAVIORAL EVOLUTION

All living animals species are successful because their behavior is well adapted to the lives they lead. Animals which are sessile, like anemones and oysters, or animals which exploit a single specialized environment, like the worms of the seashore, function well

Fig. 10-3 *At the left a male English robin displays his red breast to a trespasser on his territory. At the right are two robin models, one accurate except for the absence of a red breast and the other a mere ball of red feathers. The feathers are far more effective in eliciting defense behavior. (From D. Lack,* The Life of the Robin, *Penguin Books, Ltd.)*

with simple behavior patterns. But in each of the major lines of evolution, there are some groups who have evolved toward increasing behavioral complexity. The Arthropod line twice has led to extraordinarily complicated social groups; once with the termites and again with the bees and ants. The land Arthropods are always limited in body size. Individuals cannot grow much bigger or more complicated. Large societies have been evolved in which individuals perform extremely specialized functions. The Molluscan line has seen the evolution of squids and octopi, which have substantial behavior capabilities. And, of course, the vertebrate line has led to the versatile behavioral capacities of the primates and of man.

There is still debate and uncertainty about the stage in evolution at which learning first appears. Some investigators believe that single-celled animals, such as *Paramecium*, can be trained. So far, the experiments have always been ambiguous, and the results can be interpreted without assuming that learning has occurred. There is better evidence that the flatworm, *Planaria* can be conditioned. When the worm is given an electric shock, it pulls itself into a ball. The shock is paired with a light for many trials. The light becomes a conditioned stimulus capable of eliciting the behavior.

Earthworms can learn to crawl to one of the arms of a simple T-shaped maze. They go to a damp, dark shelter at the end of one arm and avoid the other arm, which leads to a region lined with sandpaper and then to an electric shock. Somewhere between 20 and 100 trials are needed before the animals are able to choose correctly 90 percent of the time. If the same worms are then required to learn a second maze, which involves a turn in the opposite direction, the new task requires fewer trials. When the worm has learned a maze, the head can be cut off as a crude but effective way of removing the "brain" or supra-esophageal ganglion. The operation does not eliminate the ability to crawl properly through the maze. Training must have produced changes throughout the central nervous system.

Cockroaches can learn simple mazes with fair facility. Ants can learn to run complicated mazes and their ability compares quite favorably with the performance of rats in the same maze (Figure 10-4). Comparing behavior of one species to another by this sort of method is necessarily very rough and may even be misleading. Certain animals, such as ants and rats, may be good at running mazes because they normally must learn their way about a complicated terrain. Animals who do not have this sort of problem in nature may be poor at maze learning, but have other types of exceptional behavioral capacity. When comparing the behavior of different animals, there is also a problem of selecting an effective reinforcement for the desired behavior. Cockroaches train better when they avoid light than when they are rewarded with food.

HUMAN BEHAVIOR

Man represents a true milestone in behavioral evolution. Thanks in large measure to our ability to master two types of language, verbal and mathematical, we can transmit information from generation to generation. Each

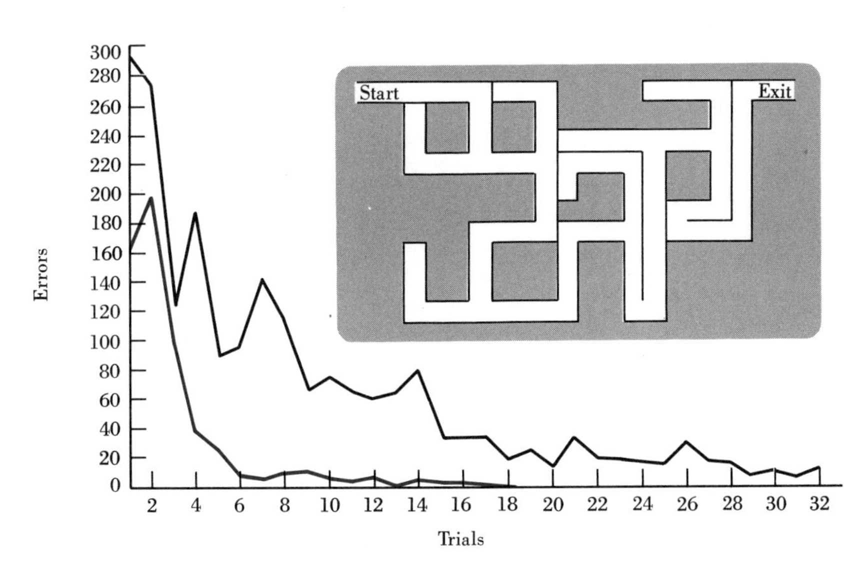

Fig. 10-4 *A maze used to compare the learning abilities of ants and of rats. The rats ran to food; the ants to their nests. The learning curves show that in this test rats learn faster than ants, but both species eventually reach a high level of performance. (Adapted from T. C. Schneirla in K. Roeder, ed.,* Insect Physiology, *1953.)*

generation can take enormous strides in developing further behavioral complexity. The behavior of our species can change with lightning speed on a completely different time scale from the slow creep of organic evolution. The advance in human behavior is based on a relatively slight increase in the ability to deal with symbols. But the relatively slight change opens up a whole new principle for acquiring, transmitting, and storing behavioral complexity.

We are often inclined to think that our behavior, by its nature, is something totally apart from that of other animals. I feel sure that this idea would rapidly disappear if we could simply spend a few hours watching our remotest ancestors who lacked the background of thousands of years of the painstaking accumulation of knowledge. Their behavior, to the detached viewer, would undoubtedly seem much closer to that of other primates than to modern man.

In trying to understand human behavior, the first inclination is to pay special attention to what the individual says. We believe that we can account for what we do. When the weight of evidence breaks this interpretation down, the next idea is that our "unconscious" can account for our behavior. From an evolutionary point of view, this is a strange and misguided assumption. We have evolved from animals who had a large repertoire of highly effective, but largely nonverbal, behavior. Is there any reason to believe that at one step in evolution an entirely new system took over the government of behavior? Much of our behavior must be governed by the same factors that determined the actions of our evolutionary ancestors.

This book has shown, in one example after another, that the only way to uncover the variables regulating the simplest activities of other animals is to undertake careful experiments. Nevertheless, it is hard to rid ourselves of the myth that we have some special insight into the factors determining our own behavior. It took many sterile years to convince experimentalists of the futility of trying to use introspective reports as the basis for uncovering the important variables determining human behavior. Introspection did not lose favor in experimental studies for philosophical reasons; it was abandoned because it simply did not work. The things a person says are a particular kind of behavior. They can be investigated by the same scientific approach that is applied to other behavior. But verbal behavior does not give any special route to the wellsprings of human conduct.

There are two reasons for raising this point at the conclusion of a book on the behavior of animals: (1) to indicate the position of man in behavioral evolution; (2) to suggest that the study of other animals is not remote from the science of human behavior. The study of behavior is a part of biology. Like other biological subjects, we will learn the most by pressing forward on the broadest possible front. Certain animals are particularly useful for settling certain types of questions. As we begin to understand the behavior of the least-complicated animals, we are laying the foundations for the study of complex behavior. The most challenging goal of the natural sciences is the understanding of human behavior. The behavioral problems prevalent in our own species add urgency to the search for understanding.

FURTHER READING

Bitterman, M. E., "The Evolution of Intelligence," *Scientific American* (January 1965), p. 92.

Brown, R. G. B., "Courtship Behavior in the *Drosophila obscura* Group, Part II, Comparative Studies," *Behaviour*, vol. 25 (1965), p. 281.

Dethier, V. G., "Communication by Insects: Physiology of Dancing," *Science*, vol. 125 (1957), p. 331.

Dilger, W. C., "The Behavior of Lovebirds," *Scientific American* (August 1962), p. 78.

Lack, D., *Darwin's Finches*. London: Cambridge University Press, 1947.

Lindauer, M., *Communication among Social Bees*. Cambridge, Mass.: Harvard University Press, 1961.

Lorenz, K. Z., "The Evolution of Behavior," *Scientific American* (December 1958), p. 67.

———, *Evolution and Modification of Behavior*. Chicago: University of Chicago Press, 1965.

Savage, J. M., *Evolution*, Modern Biology Series. New York: Holt, Rinehart and Winston, 1963.

Schneirla, T. C., "Modifiability in Insect Behavior," in *Insect Physiology*, K. D. Roeder, ed. New York: Wiley, 1953, p. 27.

Sherrington, C., *Man on His Nature*. London: Cambridge University Press, 1951.

Skinner, B. F., *Science and Human Behavior*. New York: Macmillan, 1953.

———, "The Phylogeny and Ontogeny of Behavior," *Science*, vol. 153 (1966), p. 1205.

Index

A

Acetylcholine, 35
Action potential, 23–25
Adaptation, 26
After-discharge, 19
Alpha rhythm, 117
Ant, 136, 159
Antagonistic reflexes, 20
Association areas, 100
Auditory projection areas, 83

B

Bastock, Margret, 132
Basilar membrane, 56
Bat, 73
Bee, 67–73, 122, 135–140, 154
Baboon, 146
Brain stem, 80, 99

C

Carnival, 148
Cat, 19, 28, 82, 85, 103, 110, 114
Cerebrum, 98–100
Cerebellum, 98
Chaffinch, 127
Chimpanzee, 94, 143
Circadian rhythm, 116
Clock, biological, 11, 75, 115
Coelenterates, 43–51
Cochlea, 56–60
Cochlear microphonic, 58
Cockroach, 107
Cocoon, 2–15
Color vision, 62, 68
Cone, 61, 66
Courtship, 77, 112, 131, 142
Command neuron, 119
Conditioned response, 88, 158

Consumatory behavior, 110
Corpus callosum, 100, 102–104
Cortex, 80, 98–100
Chaining, 96
Crayfish, 53

D

Dance flies, 153
Dark adaptation, 62, 65
Darwin, Charles, 151, 156
Dethier, Vincent, 155
Development, 14, 121–132
Discrimination, 94
Dog, 18, 110
Drive, 110
Drosophila, 132, 152
Ducks, 126

E

Ear, 56–59
Earthworm, 158
Eccles, John C., 28
Egg-rolling behavior, 79
Electric fish, 73
Electroencephalogram (EEG), 116–118
Emotion, 90, 112
Ethologist, 75
Excitatory postsynaptic potential (EPSP), 29–31
Extinction, 88, 90
Facilitation, 45
Fighting cock, 94, 110
Final common path, 39
Finch, 156–157
Flexion reflex, 17, 33, 37
Frisch, Karl von, 67–154
Frog, 85–86, 122

G

Ganglion cells, 60, 84
Generator potential, 54, 58
Genetics, 14, 132–134
Geographical isolation, 152
Goat, 113
Goldfish, 106
Goodall, Jane, 143
Greeting, 147

H

Habituation, 87
Hair cell, 57–58
Harlow, Harry, 128
Hearing, 56–59, 82
Hermit crab, 48
Hindbrain, 98–100
Hippocampus, 98–100, 105–106
Hormone, 4, 113, 137, 149
Hydra, 47, 109
Hypothalamus, 98–100, 113

I

Imprinting, 126
Inhibition, presynaptic, 40
Inhibitory postsynaptic potentials (IPSP), 30, 55
Instinctive behavior, 121
Interneurons, 32
Intrafusal muscle fibers, 25–28, 35–42
Irradiation, 18

L

Lashley, Karl, 100, 103
Latency, reflex, 18
Law of effect, 89
Limb transplantation, 125
Limbic system, 112
Lindauer, Martin, 139, 155
Lobster, 53
Local sign, 20
Long-term memory, 105
Lorenz, Konrad, 126
Lynx, 112
Lyonet, P., 13

M

Man, 91, 104–105, 112, 124, 159–161
Maturation, 126
Maze, 101–102, 133, 158
Messenger RNA, 107
Meyers, R., 103
Mice, 149
Milner, P., 111
Midbrain, 98–100
Monkey, 94, 103, 127–132

Monosynaptic reflex, 22
Motor cortex, 81, 100–102
Motoneuron, alpha-, 28–38, 40–42
Motoneuron, gamma-, 28, 35–37, 40–42, 55
Moth, 3, 74
Mushroom bodies, 14

N

Nematocysts, 47, 109
Neocortex, 99–102
Nerve net, 44–46
Newt, 123
Newton, Isaac, 62

O

Octopus, 104
Odor, 4, 62, 68, 155
Olds, James, 111
Olfaction, 62, 68
"One-armed" bandit, 93
Operant conditioning, 89–95
Opossum, 100

P

Pain, 112
Paleopallium, 98–100
Paramecium, 158
Pavlov, I., 88
Pacemaker, 49
Pheromone, 137
Pigeon, 64, 74, 89, 126
Planaria, 158
Play, 132, 146
Pliny, 97
Polarized light, 72
Population size, 148
Praying mantis, 41
Polysynaptic reflex, 22, 32
Punishment, 95
Puromycin, 106
Puzzle box, 89

Q

Queen substance, 136

R

Raccoon, 97
Rat, 105, 110, 159
Recurrent inhibition, 34
Reflex, definition of, 16
Reflex figure, 19
Refractory period, 24
Reinforcement, 90–97, 111, 140
Releaser, 77
REM sleep, 118
Renshaw cell, 34–35
Reproductive isolation, 152
Reticular formation, 80, 117–118
Reverberatory neuron loop, 33, 105
Retina, 60, 84, 124
Rhodopsin, 61, 65
Ring dove, 114
Robin, 157
Rod, 61, 66
Round dance, 69
RNA, 106–107

S

Scratch reflex, 21
Sea slug, 118
Secondary reinforcer, 94
Sensory projection areas, 100
Sexual behavior, 112, 131, 142, 146, 152–153
Sherrington, C. S., 17, 89
Short-term memory, 105
Silkmoth, 2
Skinner box, 89, 111
Sleep, 117
Somatic sensory cortex, 81, 101, 117
Song, 127
Spatial summation, 20, 29
Species-specific behavior, 3, 121–122
Sperry, R. W., 103
Spider, 87
Spindle organ, 22, 25–28
Split-brain animals, 103–104
Stickleback, 75, 114, 156
Stretch-bend movement pattern, 6
Stretch receptor, 22, 25–28, 52–56
Stretch reflex, 21–22, 28–30
Supranormal stimuli, 79
Swarming, 140

Swing-swing movement pattern, 7
Synapse, 22, 28–30, 44, 107

T

Telencephalon, 100
Temperature regulation, 139
Temporal summation, 20, 30, 45
Territory, 77, 141
Terry cloth mother, 128
Thalamus, 80, 99
Tinbergen, N., 77, 141
Thorndike, E. L., 89
Thorpe, W. H., 127
Threshold, 17, 23
Thirst, 110
Tool, 145, 157
Transducer, 52
Transmitter, chemical, 29, 33, 35
Tunmore's rule, 74

U

Unconditioned stimulus, 88, 96

V

Valves of cocoon, 5, 7
Vertical lobe, 105

W

Wagging dance, 69–73, 140, 154
Whelk, 48
Willows, A. O. D., 118
Wire mother, 128